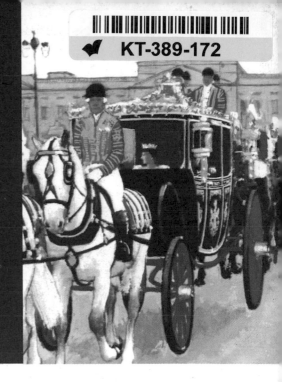

It's a FACT!

A NEW QUESTION AND ANSWER BOOK

Written by **RICHARD WRIGHT**

contents

ODHAMS BOOKS

12/6

digging up history

Coins from the past, from left to right, a copper Roman sestertius (Antoninus Pius), a silver Aethelred II penny and a silver Charles I crown, Tower Mint

Dating the sites

Dating historical sites which have been excavated is very difficult indeed. Generally layers are reliable, for layers on top must be more recent than layers lower down unless they have been drastically disturbed by rebuilding or collapse. Coins and pieces of pottery are the most helpful objects for they have had a wide distribution and a lot is known about them. But now scientists are helping by analysing the actual objects found. Some forms of carbon, such as Carbon 14, are radio-active and their rate of discharge can be accurately measured so that the chemist can offer fairly precise dates. Soil analysis can also reveal much about the type of people and how they lived.

Spotting from the air

During the Second World War archaeology received unexpected help from aerial photographic surveys. White lines and plans of buildings appeared on the ground's surface for no apparent reason in the photographs. Excavation revealed streets and buildings not far beneath the surface of the soil. The reason why the remains show up well in aerial photographs is that shallow earth soon becomes dry and shows up paler. Often these lines appear in droughts but disappear after a wet spell. The technique is now widespread, and has resulted in some of the most interesting finds of our time, for despite the most diligent of searches the remains are often invisible on the ground.

An aerial photograph of Maiden Castle, an ancient earthwork in Dorset, England

Hidden treasure

Thanks to excellent coverage on television, archaeology is now a widespread interest with all kinds of people who are curious about the long-distant way of life of past ages. The old hope of discovering hidden treasure is certainly equally strong, particularly with younger folk. And well it might be, for the two classes of people who seem to have the best prospects of "chance" finds are schoolboys and outdoor workers, such as farm labourers and building demolition men. Rivers are also a fruitful source, and some big finds have been made by fishermen.

Now comes the question: if I find something in the ground which looks old or valuable, can I keep it? The law must be brought in, for the Crown has important rights in treasure trove. Your local museum curator will help you determine the nature of your find, and will probably undertake the whole business of settling the matter with the coroner if he thinks your find is of sufficient value. The purchase of the object is then arranged fairly with the finder. Shapeless objects of lesser value often mean a great deal to archaeologists, but have little monetary worth. If you take them to your museum to help further their work of discovering the past, you will be well rewarded by the new friends you will make. Some museum curators run clubs for ordinary people who are interested in the subject and which make frequent visits to historical sites.

King John's treasure

One of the most famous legends of buried treasure in Britain involves King John. The king's baggage train containing his treasure is said to have been swept away by the incoming tide while crossing The Wash in East Anglia in 1216. Precious stones, gold cups, silver plate, sceptres and jewellery of great value were lost. Despite many organised searches, no pieces have ever been recovered, but in recent years drillings in farmland reclaimed from the sea have revealed traces of gold.

The Sutton Hoo burial ship and some of the treasure found aboard it in 1939

A ship burial

One of the richest historical finds ever made in England was in 1939 on the banks of the River Debden at Sutton Hoo in East Anglia. Eleven burial barrows were found and the largest yielded the burial ship. The ship was a sea-going rowing boat about 1,300 years old and which had been let into a trench on dry land. The burial part amidships was roofed over with oak boards. Fortunately the treasure it contained was too deeply embedded in the sand for it to have been looted by thieves. The boat was nearly ninety feet long and was designed for thirty or forty rowers, yet strangely enough no human bones were found. The treasure hoard was probably the personal possessions of a great Pagan leader who very likely was of royal rank. Some of the domestic articles come from the other end of the Mediterranean, and amongst the enormous drinking horns is one that held six pints. The personal equipment of the warrior-leader is very rich in heavy gold and ornamentation. The precise date of the ship is unknown, but some Frankish coins found in a very beautiful purse have been dated at around A.D. 650. The burial, therefore, could not have been made before that date, though the ship could be older. Due to the Second World War this important find went into storage for seven years, but careful restoration by experts after the war has preserved it for posterity. It can now be seen in the British Museum in London.

feats of the ancient world

Hannibal crossing the Alps on his way to war in Italy

One man against Rome

It was in Sicily that the young vigorous republic of Rome first came into collision with the Carthaginians who ruled the trade of the Mediterranean with an iron hand. The Romans were landsmen but they built fleets specially for the war and even trained men to row on dry land. The Roman losses were appalling but always they built more ships and raised more men until finally by sheer ruthless determination the Carthaginians were driven out and Sicily became the first Roman province.

In the uneasy peace that followed, both sides prepared for future war. At that time, a small boy, destined to become one of the world's greatest generals, was led to the altar in Spain and made to swear eternal hatred to the Romans. The boy was Hannibal.

On reaching manhood, Hannibal forced war on Rome and attacked by the land route which meant crossing the Alps with his famous elephants in bad weather and amid hostile tribes. The journey took months and cost him a quarter of his troops. But once in Italy, he crushed several Roman armies with masterful ease so that North Italy was abandoned to him. However, Rome's allies stood firm and the new policy of containing him without offering open battle weakened him, for no supplies came from Carthage. But his genius remained and he escaped at will from all his enemy's traps. Yet he badly needed supplies and at last his brother, Hasdrubal, forced his way through from Spain, only to be defeated. His severed head was thrown into Hannibal's camp.

Rome now attacked Carthage itself and Hannibal was recalled from Italy, where he had campaigned for fifteen years, to defend the city. When Carthage fell, Hannibal fled to Rome's enemies in the east. Eventually they were defeated and his surrender became the price of peace. Learning this, Hannibal preferred to take his own life.

The Pygmies and the Giant

The Greeks of Asia Minor came just within the western limits of the large and unwieldy Persian Empire and it was not long before they revolted against the indignity of paying tribute. In this revolt they were helped by the Athenians and other mainland Greeks who thus brought themselves unfavourably to the notice of Darius who decided to send his colossal forces to annihilate them.

The approach of the land forces was so slow that Darius sent a great fleet with 20,000 professional soldiers

6

across the Aegean. This force met the Athenians together with a few hundred men from Plataea at Marathon. Meanwhile, Pheidippides had been sent on his famous run to warn Sparta but by the time the Spartans arrived, the outnumbered Athenians had already won the day and sent the Persians scurrying for home. Ten years later, Xerxes came with an enormous army to avenge the defeat of Darius. All seemed lost. Southwards the colossus rolled into Greece which was then not a country but a collection of highly independent tiny city states. This time Sparta took the first brunt of the attack. At the narrow pass of Thermopylae, Leonidas with his three hundred Spartans delayed the whole Persian advance until they were cut down to the last man. This heroic stand, however, only saved time. By land and sea, the Persians poured on to attack Athens. After bitter debate, the Athenians decided to stake their whole existence on a single throw. They evacuated their women, children and old people to

nearby islands, abandoned the beautiful city, and the fighting men took to the sea. Then, led by the Athenians, the Greek fleet broke the Persian navy at Salamis. Weakened by disease and famine, the helpless army recoiled and Xerxes went home in disgust. These three incredible victories by tiny Greece saved them and gave the leadership of the world to the West.

Aqueduct of Carthage

During the Roman colonisation of the ancient city of Carthage, the Emperor Hadrian ordered the construction of an aqueduct to bring water to the city from Jebel Zaghwan nearly 60 miles away. Begun in A.D. 117 and completed in A.D. 161 the aqueduct had arches 49 feet high and spanned 56 miles. Today only $7\frac{1}{2}$ miles remain standing.

Star records

The Babylonians were magnificent astronomers. They had star records that went back for 360 years which is a longer period of time than any modern records possess. They also worked out the length of the year within an error of 27 minutes. Also today we have 60 minutes and 60 seconds because Babylonian mathematics were based on a 60-system.

The Greeks' victory over the Persians at Salamis

feats of the ancient world

continued

Pyramids

The Great Pyramid of Giza is almost five thousand years old and, according to Herodotus, 100,000 men worked on it for 20 years. Save for the small burial chamber of the Pharaoh, it is a solid mass of 2,300,000 blocks of dressed stone, each averaging two and a half tons. Such a feat was possible only in a country where the ruler was both god and king. The four sides of the base are pitched north, south, east and west, with only a fractional error. The whole building was erected by slave power and leverage, the wheel being unknown in Egypt in those days.

Miletus

Civilisation owes a great debt to Ancient Greece in which Athens ranked supreme. But the Greeks of Asia Minor were equally brilliant, in particular those of Miletus. Thales, traveller, astronomer and man of affairs, used Babylonian records to predict an eclipse of the sun in 585 B.C. Such accuracy was the sensation of the Ancient World, and began man's freedom from superstition. Other Greek thinkers believed that the universe was subject to definite laws, and like Hecataeus, who drew a map of the Ancient World, they began to record their findings.

The lighthouse at the port of Alexandria

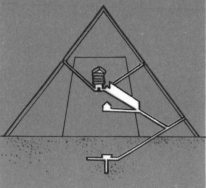

The great pyramid of Giza built by slaves

Alexandria

Alexandria, founded by Alexander the Great, was the greatest port of the Mediterranean and the most famous Greek university town. Its lighthouse of Pharos was one of the Seven Wonders of the World. It stood 445 feet high and endured for 1,600 years. The University was particularly famous for mathematics and medicine. Euclid, Archimedes and the great doctor Galen were among its teachers. It was in Egypt that Eratosthenes measured the earth by using the reflections of the noon sun in water wells to determine the change of angle. Further, the great library with its hundreds of thousands of rolls recorded their work, and organised a system of accurate copyists who issued books to the whole of the Ancient World on paper.

The dome of the Pantheon in Rome, built during the reign of the Emperor Hadrian

Roman concrete

No one who has looked at the remains of Roman buildings can have failed to notice the marvellous quality of the concrete. Neither weather nor decay seem to have affected it, whereas many modern concretes show the effects of wear very quickly. The Emperor Hadrian ordered a marvellous single-cast dome for the roof of the Pantheon in Rome. The concrete dome is 142 feet across supported only by its outside walls.

The first Suez Canal

The modern Suez Canal is not yet a hundred years old but the idea of a connecting link between the Red Sea and the Mediterranean by water is very old. About 4,000 years ago a canal was dug from the Red Sea to the nearest branch of the Nile. By using the nearest point of the Red Sea and the most easterly branch of the Delta, the distance was not great. The fleets of the Pharaoh could travel far and speedily.

Stonehenge, situated on Salisbury Plain, in Wiltshire

Stonehenge

For centuries this monument of prehistoric Britain has intrigued all who have a love of the past. Although it was probably an open-air temple of some sort, its precise use is not yet known, and it certainly owes nothing to the Druids (though they may have used it much later.) The work was commenced soon after 2000 B.C. and the main part dates back to about 1500 B.C. Great skill has been used, for the great stone archways are connected downwards and sideways and carefully shaped to follow the curve of a circle. The large sarsen, or sandstone, stones, which are over 22 feet in height and weigh many tons, are local; but the smaller blue stones have been brought from the Prescelly Mountains in Pembrokeshire – a distance of over 200 miles by land or sea. Some scientists have advanced the theory that Stonehenge was a computer for working out the movements of the stars and planets. But Stonehenge still remains a mystery – perhaps forever.

IT'S A FACT!

The conquests of Alexander the Great made Greek the best-known language of the world into which Jesus was born and thus the New Testament came to be written in Greek.

The Babylonians had a story of a great flood in which a man and his wife were saved in a large ship.

The oldest known aqueduct was constructed by Sennacherib of Assyria to bring fresh water to Nineveh. It was over 900 feet long and nearly 80 feet wide.

The famous hanging gardens of Babylon seem to have been a series of garden terraces on top of the imperial palace.

Craftsmen living in the Danube Valley about 1,800 B.C. first invented a sword strong enough to strike with, as opposed to the old thrusting sword.

Schliemann, who discovered Troy and other early Greek cities, was a poor boy who taught himself Greek and one day intended to prove Homer right. Later he made a fortune and carried out his life-long ambition where many scholars had failed.

The main cause of the extensive ruins of the Parthenon was the explosion of a Turkish powder magazine stored there in 1687.

The elephants, famous in Carthaginian armies, were mainly used as living "tanks" to tear holes in the ranks of the enemy through which the Carthaginians could rush and upset the opposing battle lines.

To show his contempt of the Senate, the young and half-mad Emperor Caligula made his horse a consul.

The little city of Pompeii was overwhelmed by the sudden eruption of Vesuvius in A.D. 79 and, now that it has been excavated from the ashes, gives us today a living portrait of a Roman town about its everyday affairs.

animal homes

Shown here, beavers building a dam, and the underwater entrance to their lodge

The snail

The garden snail belongs to a race of soft-bodied creatures that must have a shell for protection and which are able to withdraw inside it. The shell is lifeless and is formed by a secretion from the snail mixed with lime. It is made in sections but keeps pace with the growth of the snail. The snail travels along on its belly.

The snail carries its home on its back

The hermit crab

This type of crab has the misfortune to be armoured only on the forepart of its body and consequently is open to fatal attack. It therefore seeks a home for its rear part and usually chooses a whelk shell. Sometimes it destroys and ejects the whelk first. The hermit crab then backs in to its new home. It is specially adapted to fit into any type and it has suckers to hold on with. Unfortunately the shell cannot grow and the hermit crab has the human problem of seeking better quarters from time to time.

The beaver

The beaver is one of the largest rodents, being about two and a half feet long. He spends his whole life close to water and mainly in it. Once beavers lived in England as the name Beverley in Yorkshire shows, but today they are only found in quantity in North America. Since the beaver requires a good depth of water to swim in when the surface water is frozen, he has become Nature's finest dam engineer. Having picked his spot expertly, he sets about building his lodge. The main material is tree logs. First he fells some trees with his powerful incisor teeth and then strips off the branches and cuts the trunks into suitable lengths. Often he makes small canals to float his timber in order to save the labour of dragging it overland. The work is done at night and the beavers work in teams. Large logs are placed at the base and then small ones on top, the cracks being filled in with clay and turf. The lodge is then watertight and when frozen above ground is safe against enemies. The entrance is underwater and there are two rooms, one for living and one for the winter food supply.

Young swallows in their open nest of mud

Swallow's nest

The swallow is an elegant exciting bird which spends as little time as possible on the ground. It arrives in April as a messenger of summer from southern Africa and builds its odd saucer-shaped nest of mud high in the rafters of barns and similar places. The martin belongs to the same family and has the same habits but it is smaller and slower than the swallow and the forked tail is stubbier. The mud nest of the martin is ball-shaped and is usually pitched under the eaves of houses. It is larger than the swallow's and the young birds often stay on to help rear the later broods.

The mole colony

Moles, which are pleasant furry little creatures to our sight, are very destructive and are usually hunted or trapped by farmers and gardeners. Almost blind and deaf, they live underground in a colony which has a largish central chamber surrounded by two circular galleries, one above the other. The mole's fur grows upright so that it does not brake him when going backwards or forwards.

Storks

Storks do not come to England but they have great similarity to herons which are members of the same order. There are many types of storks but the ones very popular in Holland, Belgium and Germany are the White Storks. These large birds are the ones which figure in the children's stories and they like to make their large nests of sticks and to pitch them high up on chimney stacks and other vantage points. They are considered to be lucky birds and the inhabitants of the Low Countries often erect platforms in handy places in order to persuade them to make their nests and to settle in the neighbourhood.

Storks nesting on chimney stacks

The uninvited guest

Many creatures in Nature live on unwilling hosts and are known as parasites. The English Cuckoo, which announces the coming of summer, is one of these unsocial creatures. In a normal season, the hen lays about fifteen eggs in the nests of other birds for them to rear and the young cuckoos are often tough enough to oust the true nestlings in order to get their share of food. Cuckoos are able to modify the size and colouring of their eggs, and also the incubation period is slightly shorter to help them with their deceitful work.

English honey bees live together in a community, in a nest constructed of wax

Bees and ants

Bees and ants belong to the same group of living things and have many very similar traits. Both these insects live in large highly organised communities and have no personal life of their own. Their home is the community: they have no home in the private sense at all but they are never short of company. There are thousands of different kinds of ants who live mostly in the Tropics. The colony of ants is grouped round the one or two perfect females who are the Queens. The numerous imperfect females are workers and have no offspring. The English Honey Bee constructs a honeycomb for its young which is a double layer of six-sided cells with a small space between just permitting the passage of a bee. The brood are reared in the lower part of the comb. The Queen Bee, the passive centre of all this intense activity, has neither a pollen basket like an ordinary bee nor the ability to produce the wax with which the honey cells are made. She is concerned solely with the next generation and but for the attendant workers she would die.

toys of the past

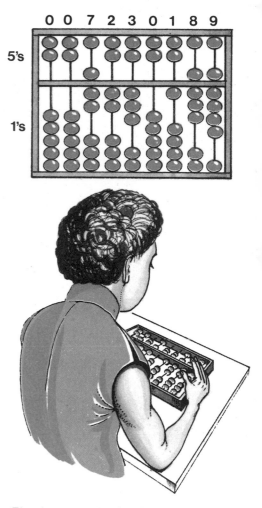

The abacus

In this country the abacus is a toy which is often placed rather hopefully on the playpen of very young children and they bang the pretty beads to and fro happily. Actually, the abacus is a simple calculating machine and is used seriously in the bazaars of the East and in shops and offices in China. It usually takes the form of a wire frame on which beads are mounted. Units are in the first row, tens in the second, hundreds in the third, and so on. The beads can be manipulated by an expert at a remarkable speed and a good operator can work as fast as a modern adding machine operated manually.

Egyptian working toy with jointed limbs

Egyptian working toys

The Egyptians were fine carpenters as their surviving work in the British Museum shows. It is not surprising, therefore, that they were able to make working toys in wood for their children. These toys were usually human or animal figures with jointed limbs to which independent movement could be given. The jaws of animals were also pivoted and could be opened and shut by a string pulled through a hole. These toys were the ancestors of puppets and modern mechanical toys.

The abacus – a simple calculating machine

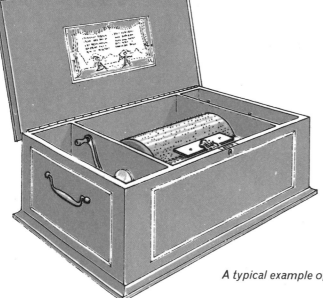

The musical box

Today we associate the musical box with Switzerland and Alpine holidays and this is correct for the musical box is a toy which the clock and watch makers created. The first automatic music came with church clocks which chimed the hours or even played a simple hymn. By 1780 there were musical watches in Geneva which could play two tunes. Gradually more complicated and expensive musical boxes were constructed with little figures that could perform tricks and dances to the tinkling music of the box.

A typical example of an old musical box

The doll

The oldest toy in any part of the world is the doll. The first dolls were made of baked clay and had neither arms nor legs, but they were the first of a line which leads to the magnificent sophisticated dolls of today. The famous wooden dolls of the past were made mainly in Holland and called Dutch dolls but their days were numbered when the toymakers of France learned to make the modern porcelain doll which resembles the living child.

Miniatures

Throughout history miniatures for children have been made of men, animals, weapons and furniture. They faithfully reflect both the age and the country where they were made so that children could immediately recognise they had smaller editions of something their parents owned.

The dolls' house

The doll has always been the commonest toy and it was not surprising that dolls' houses came into being. Some are merely upright boxes hinged at the front to open and reveal the interior. Of all the elaborate ones, the most famous is Queen Mary's dolls' house which is now on show at Windsor Castle.

Toy theatre

Toy theatres are a modern growth beginning in the 19th century but occurring all over western Europe and patronised by some remarkably famous names. Originally they were souvenir sheets of theatre artists and scenery which were published and seized on by children for cutting out and mounting. The traditional price became one penny plain and two-penny coloured.

Toy soldiers

The wholesale manufacture of toy soldiers cast in solid lead began in Germany. Later, English toymakers learnt to produce hollow-cast toy soldiers with a great saving in expensive metal and "tin soldiers" in brilliant colours became a leading feature of English boys' toys.

One of the more elaborate toy theatres

A rocking horse

The rocking horse

Before the coming of the motor car, the horse was the only means of swift travel and naturally every boy and girl wanted to have one. Not many were fortunate enough but the rocking horse became the nearest substitute. As they improved, they were superbly made to resemble beautiful and spirited horses complete with stirrups and reins. The sharply curved rockers enabled a good speed to be attained and the result was very satisfying for the children.

IT'S A FACT!

Toys of the rattle and drum type for making a joyful noise appear very early in all countries.

Clockwork toys, driven by a strong spring wound by a key, first gave moving mechanical toys to millions of children and came from Germany.

The hoop and the ball were used in Ancient Egypt.

When times were poorer, the scooter was the common form of transport for the British child.

Roman girls gave their childhood dolls as an offering to the goddess Venus when they were about to marry.

Fivestones is an old game that used to be played with sheep's knuckles.

The true game of marbles has many forms and is highly complicated and quite unlike the straight-forward knock-out game usually played today.

The most famous and costly Easter-eggs ever produced were made by the great jeweller, Fabergé, for the children of the Russian Imperial family. Each egg opened to reveal a jewelled surprise.

The model ships made by sailors for boys and inserted into bottles were put in with their masts down. They were so hinged that they could be drawn erect by a thread from outside.

Jigsaw puzzles were first made by London mapmakers in the 18th century and some of the first puzzles were maps.

A favourite toy of the past was a Noah's Ark with a complete zoo of wooden animals to go with it and to be hurriedly packed against the disaster.

The kite comes from the East, particularly from China, and in that country there is a special festival called "Climbing the Heights" when kites are flown all over the land.

13

hot and cold deserts

The Magga Dan (1,957 tons), a British Antarctic expeditionary ship

Hot deserts

Hot deserts, where man and beast will swiftly die if they remain exposed to the fierce heat, cover about a seventh of the world's land surface. They are strung round the world in two ragged belts roughly corresponding to the Tropics of Cancer and Capricorn. The fierce fight for survival is based on resisting the terrible heat and conserving every drop of precious water. Of the men and women who live in the desert, some wear no real clothing, while others wear fold after fold of protective cloth.

Insects and reptiles endure the harsh conditions well but birds have to migrate during the hottest periods. Many desert creatures practise aestivation. Some toads, for example, bury themselves for months during the greatest heat until the peril passes. The camel is remarkable in that his special hump of fat serves as a water reserve. Many plants hide water inside themselves or underground and when rain does come, the desert is temporarily transformed into a land of vivid flowers, as the response to the brief rainy spells is exceptionally rapid.

The inside of an igloo (left) and below, an Eskimo driving his husky dog team

14

Cold deserts

The cold deserts occur at both the Poles but only near the North Pole are human settlements found. People who live in these icy wastes are all small both in height and size. Vegetation is not much use to the Polar peoples but the seas abound with fish and seals. Consequently the people are mainly fishers and hunters under conditions of the most severe cold. In winter, Eskimos travel on the frozen snow and ice but in the time of thaw, they travel by boat.

The civilised world has greatly changed the peoples of the North Pole for air routes between Europe and North America cross their homes and the fishing industries are now extremely valuable. The life of the Eskimo has been transformed. He can now buy tinned goods and uses an outboard motor. Arctic aerodromes are glad of his services, and, to everyone's surprise, the Eskimo is proving a natural mechanic. But with the help and interest of the European and American, the life of Polar peoples is changing rapidly as their old customs become outdated.

Camels – "ships of the desert" – can travel for a considerable time without water

Mirages are optical illusions caused by the bending of light by layers of air at very different temperatures.

Penguins are found only at the South Pole while Polar Bears are found only at the North.

The Sahara is the biggest desert in the world and has 3 million inhabitants.

Desert animals are mainly nocturnal and do not come out in the noon-day heat.

There is a tremendous drop in temperature between night and day in the desert.

The low entrance to an igloo is designed to keep out the cold and the visits of polar bears who are very fierce.

Vultures can see dying animals from miles away. Their bodies are very light and can drift tirelessly on the warm air currents.

The Arctic Summer lasts on average about two months when there is continuous daylight for twenty four hours.

If it is fed with green vegetation, the camel can go for weeks without water. It can endure the loss of a quarter of its entire weight without serious damage.

The Northern Lights

Aurora Borealis or Northern Lights is the name given to a glowing, natural light which can be seen at night in the sky of the Northern Hemisphere. This light is given off when gases floating above the earth are hit by electric particles from the sun. Aural displays usually take place about 70 miles above the earth's surface during which the colour green, caused by atomic oxygen, is that most commonly seen.

The Aurora Borealis, or Northern Lights

15

unusual buildings

The Monument

This stone tower stands at one end of London Bridge to mark Pudding Lane, the spot where the Great Fire of 1666 started. The unsupported tower is simply one vast column of the Greek Doric type. Designed by Wren and erected by the City of London's architect, it stands over two hundred feet high. Inside the Monument stone steps lead up to the top and on payment of a fee the public can climb and obtain a view of London which in the seventeenth century commanded the whole city.

The George Inn

In a narrow yard off Southwark High Street, London, can be found the George Inn which is all that is left of the riotous South Bank, so famous in Shakespeare's days. Here were the great coaching inns from which travellers set out for the coast. Originally the inns had galleries surrounding all sides of the courtyard but today only one side of one inn remains – The George. It was these galleried inns which were used by actors and they served as models for the theatres which Shakespeare and his partners built.

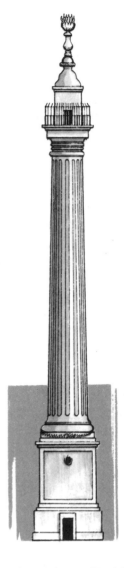

The George Inn (left) near Southwark High Street, London and right, The Monument

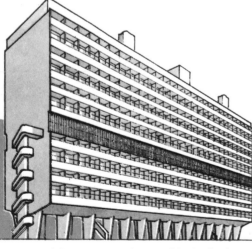

A housing unit designed by Le Corbusier

The Eiffel Tower

This tower which bears the name of its creator has dominated the Paris skyline from its position on the Champ de Mars for nearly eighty years. Eiffel had a world reputation as an engineer and he was invited to construct this tower for the great Paris Exhibition of 1889. It took three years to build and used 7,500 tons of iron. The four legs of the tower unite to form three platforms and the top one is 985 feet above Paris. Today the tower is used as a radio and television station.

The Ariel Hotel (below) situated near London Airport and right, the Eiffel Tower

Large-scale building

The modern tendency is to build skyscrapers and very large units in our cities. This development has enabled architects to provide amenities, such as car parks and gardens, in the space saved on the ground. Our picture shows a modern building raised on stilts, or pilotis, in order to preserve the view at ground level. The most famous name in this type of total planning is Le Corbusier who designed whole cities.

The Ariel Hotel

In 1847, two British engineers made a heavier-than-air model aeroplane which was driven by steam. It was the first break-through to powered flight and the circular hotel next to London Airport was so named because they felt their building was a similar break-through against aircraft noise. Not only is the building circular to allow maximum airflow round it but it has extensive soundproofing and a system of air-conditioning.

Martello Towers

Round the coast of south-east England, particularly in Kent and Sussex, there are still a great number of these sturdily built round towers standing about forty feet high. They are really forts and were constructed as part of the coastal defences to keep out Napoleon should he ever launch his invasion forces against England, which was a real danger at the time. The name comes from Martello Point in Corsica where a similar fort resisted the battery of Admiral Hood's guns with unexpected success. But Napoleon did not come and the forts were never used.

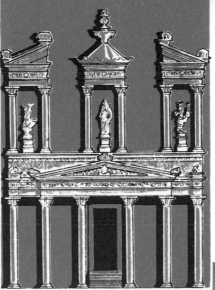

The Temple at Petra, carved from rock

Rock temples at Petra

Petra was once an important town on the caravan routes and goes back to Roman and early Christian times but it has long been allowed to fall into ruin. The great traveller, Burckhardt, rediscovered it in 1812. The town lies in a steep-sided basin of sandstone and the most exciting approach is from the east through a narrow gorge. Then all about him the amazed traveller sees the tombs and temples – there are over seven hundred – which have been cut in the face of the living rock.

A Martello tower, built in the 19th century

The Taj Mahal, India, built almost entirely of marble

The Taj Mahal

This superb building at Agra in India is actually a tomb. It took twenty-two years to construct and was begun in 1630 by Shah Jehan, a Moghul Emperor, in memory of his favourite wife who had died the previous year, giving birth to her fourteenth child. Made almost entirely in white marble, the building has a cool beauty against the blue sky and the harmony of the whole is matched by the detailed workmanship, for thousands of semi-precious stones are sunk in its walls.

Wren's Guildhall, Windsor

The Guildhall, Windsor

This charming building which juts out inconveniently into the main street of Windsor was designed by Sir Christopher Wren and amusingly illustrates the difficulties which even the greatest architects have to face. The stone pillars which support the upper room do not actually touch the roof which they are supposed to support; there is a gap of about two inches. The reason is that although Wren said they were unnecessary the authorities insisted that he put them in. He did, but two inches short to prove his point that they were not needed.

the encircling sea

Polar bear diving for food below the ice

Underwater storms

Everyone is accustomed to great changes on the surface of the sea caused by different patterns of wave movement or the changing seasons but when we assume that the sea beneath the surface is at rest, we are quite wrong. There is a strange level which seamen call "dead water" where the surface water meets the internal waves of the sea. Violent collisions occur between the ocean currents and tidal movements which try to cross them, setting up dangerous turbulence. Submarines are often tossed about like corks underwater. Waves set up by underwater earthquakes and wrongly called "tidal" also send fantastic forces through the world's seas, sometimes killing fish who are flung out of their proper areas.

Monsters of the deep

Not far from the warm, shallow waters which surround the land, the sea bed plunges down long slopes towards the ocean floor. Cold and dark grow ever more intense as the bed drops down to the icy blackness which exists at the bottom. Vegetation gradually dies as the descent goes on. It is rather like climbing a mountain in reverse. Soon the only food is other fish and these long, dark slopes are the homes of the great killer fish who live by eating others. There, fierce and merciless battles are fought out between the giant squids and the largest fish in the sea who bear the scars of the squids' tentacles on their heads for life. Other deep ocean fish have telescopic eyes to catch the small amount of light, heavily armoured bodies to withstand the pressure, and fierce teeth and claws to help them survive the grim battle. As yet, very little is known about this world far below the surface.

Where is Atlantis?

Among early peoples there are persistent records of lost lands under the sea. The most famous of these stories concerns Atlantis from which the Atlantic Ocean takes its name. In the long history of the earth, the sea has covered and uncovered the dry land many times and in many ways. Occasionally, early man may have seen the remains of settlements which were revealed by smaller movements of the sea. Also in historic times coastal places have first been cut off then submerged so that there was a certain amount of proof that lost cities might exist under the waves. But the famous lost cities, of which Atlantis is the most renowned, are almost certainly mythical.

As Plato tells the story of Atlantis, it was a lost island or continent lying out in the dangerous ocean west of the Pillars of Hercules, the old name for the Straits of Gibraltar. Marauders from Atlantis frequently made war on the Mediterranean peoples but one day the mysterious land disappeared under the waves when it was destroyed by an earthquake. However, no trace of any such land or island has ever been found to give substance to the old tales, although marauders may well have come from this direction in early times.

In search of Atlantis, a Greek ship sailing between the Pillars of Hercules

The brilliant white chalk cliffs of the Seven Sisters situated in Southern England

Thor Heyerdahl's raft, Kon-Tiki

The Kon-Tiki

Not all the stories of the past are un-true, as the wonderful voyage of the Kon-Tiki proved. Thor Heyerdahl, a Norwegian scientist, visited the Poly-nesian islands in the middle of the Pacific and became fascinated by the problem of how these people ever came to be there. Having decided that they must have come from Peru, he and five daring companions built a tradi-tional Indian raft of balsa wood and sailed the 4,300 miles from Peru to Polynesia using only a single sail and the prevailing currents. This hazardous voyage lasted 101 days and proved the origins of the Polynesians.

In his diaries, Thor Heyerdahl re-marked on the many strange fish which came up at night to inspect the silent raft as it glided through the water like the old sailing ships. Some of these fish were previously thought to be extinct and others were quite unknown but not unlike some of those which had featured in the sailors' yarns which no one had believed. At night the luminous eyes of the fish ringed the craft like the headlights of ghostly cars.

The white cliffs of Dover

The chalk hills of England are something like the spokes of a wheel running out from Salisbury Plain across southern and eastern England. They were very important to early man who used them as trackways which were warm, dry and bare of trees so that his enemies could not lurk in ambush. Farming took place remarkably high up on these downs and the heavily wooded and sodden valleys were not used very much at that time. Near the centre of this complex of hills stands Stonehenge, the ancient monument we only partly understand despite all our efforts.

Today, the chalk hills mean beautiful rolling downs and dazzling white cliffs which greet the returning traveller as he steams into Dover. Yet these cliffs, which stand now like bastions against the sea, were actually formed under it in the most incredible way. The chalk is made up of the tiny shells and skeletons of billions and billions of minute creatures which lived and died in the warm, clear sea which once covered southern Europe and northern Africa. The water was shallow and so pure that it is thought that desert must have surrounded it. For endless ages, the tiny white specks drifted down until, in the fullness of time, the hundreds of feet of chalk cliff and swelling down were built up. Today, the sea batters against the chalk, slowly taking back the hills which it gave to the land.

Two of the strange creatures to be found in the deep waters of the ocean

19

the encircling sea *continued*

Legends of the sea

From out of the vast and violent loneliness of the sea have come many stories of lost cities and incredible monsters but some of the strangest stories concern true events. For centuries derelict ships have cruised madly about the oceans without crews, lights or control, a danger to shipping, wherever the currents and winds took them. Most of these unsinkable ships were wooden sailing ships with light cargoes which floated on and on. Today it is a routine task of a modern navy to sink such dangerous wrecks by gunfire.

Much stranger are the deserted ships like the *Mary Celeste*. This sailing ship left New York for Genoa in 1872 and was found near Gibraltar completely deserted. However, the sails were set and the cargo was intact. The only sign of the interruption of normal life was a half-eaten meal on a table. Otherwise everything was in order except that no trace of the crew has ever been found since.

Dutch farmland, created by reclaiming land once covered by the sea

Stealing from the sea

In no country in the world is the sea more involved with the land than in Holland where only by an elaborate system of dykes and canals has the neat, intensively cultivated and cared-for little country been able to keep the sea at bay. Most people recognise the coast of Holland on the map of Europe by the circular bite made in its outline by the Zuider Zee. But this familiar landmark is gradually disappearing as the Dutch progressively cut back the sea and create new farmland, called Polders.

Amsterdam waterfront and right, some Dutch fishing vessels

The deserted sailing ship, Mary Celeste

The city of herrings

Herrings are a great delicacy to the people of Amsterdam. It is quite possible to see a smartly dressed businessman go to a herring stall, take a herring, hold it aloft, eat it down, and then go off to his appointment. This loyalty to the herring is well deserved from a city which owes its origin so much to fishermen and their ways. The story goes back to the Middle Ages when the fish supply was even more important as a source of fresh food. Then, as now, the fishermen followed the shoals and studied their movements. Suddenly the fish changed their breeding grounds. No one knows what change in the sea caused this migration, but they left their haunts off Denmark and Norway and moved south. The fishermen followed and made a small port for themselves where Amsterdam now stands.

Men on the Dogger Bank

This famous fishing ground is really a plateau, about the size of Denmark, lying some sixty feet under the waters of the North Sea. Some tens of thousands of years ago it was dry land and today the trawlers bring up in their nets not only the bones of bison, mammoth and other animals of the time but also the flint tools of early man.

IT'S A FACT!

The warmth of Spring brings the sea to life in the same way that it does the land but the change is much more rapid.

Basically, ocean currents spin to the right in the northern hemisphere but to the left in the southern hemisphere.

The great saucer shape in which the Pacific Ocean now rests is thought by scientists to have been made when the moon was torn away from the earth.

The Sargasso Sea has the saltiest seawater in the world.

A wave over a hundred feet high has been scientifically recorded.

The Persian Gulf has the hottest seawater in the world.

Three quarters of the surface of our planet is ocean.

The sea is not silent beneath the waves. The extensive use of hydrophones by modern navies has shown that fish can communicate over long distances under water.

facts about fish

Fish move in a medium eight hundred times denser than air. Thus the need for streamlining causes the fish to keep the same shape, though not the same size, from its birth to its death.

Small fish do not swim as rapidly as they appear to do. They have quick acceleration but little stamina to sustain it. Ten times its own length in a second, kept up for about a minute, appears to be the limit for the speed of a fish.

Most fish with bones also have a special swimbladder inside their bodies which enables them to hover almost without effort. From this point they can take off in any direction.

Electric eels have special organs which consist of columns, each containing thousands of electro-plates. Most of these are connected in series thus adding up to a very large voltage for a brief burst. These natural batteries take up half the length of the eel.

Three deep-sea fishermen setting out in their

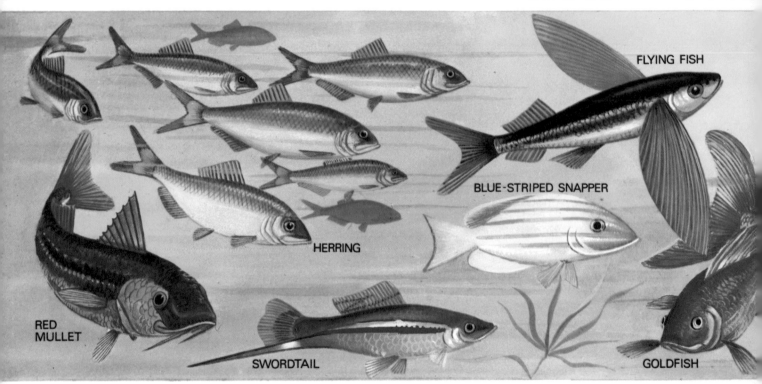

FLYING FISH

BLUE-STRIPED SNAPPER

HERRING

RED MULLET

SWORDTAIL

GOLDFISH

All fish work hard for their oxygen. There is not much oxygen in water compared with air and a great deal of water is passed through the gills to extract sufficient oxygen for the needs of the fish.

Most of the very good food which we obtain from fish comes from the massive swimming muscles. In fish like the giant tunny, three quarters of the body is muscle.

Twenty seconds is a long time for a flying fish to be airborne in the Pacific Ocean, most flights are much less, but the longest flights cover several hundred yards.

Most jawed fish breathe by taking in water through their mouths, pumping over the gills where the oxygen is extracted, and driving the remainder out through special openings in the skin behind the gills.

Fish, which live a long time, continue to grow after reaching maturity. The increased swimming speed and stamina range which comes with size helps them to do this.

In general, fish have not as highly developed nervous systems as men but, through their skin, they are very sensitive to the slightest disturbance in the water.

There are some air-breathing fish and they are the ancestors of both the amphibians and man. These fish live in marginal areas between sea and land and use their lungs to survive in a dry season.

Fish are cold-blooded animals that have no means of keeping a constant body temperature but they "adopt" the temperature of the waters in which they live.

Some of the fish with weaker electrical powers put out an electric field round themselves which probably helps them both to avoid obstacles and to identify prey.

powerful motor boat for a good day's sport

IT'S A FACT!

The eye of a fish has a special lens which protrudes more than a normal eye. Consequently, two such eyes, set in the side of the head, give the fish all-round vision on both sides of his body.

Fish are long-sighted and can see for good distances.

A man with an aqualung places himself in the position of a fish with a swimbladder, he can move anywhere from his point of rest.

For fish, smooth regular movements are safe whereas any jerky, splashy movements attract the attention of the killers.

Some of the scavenger fish grind their hard broken food with the sand that they swallow until it becomes a fine consumable paste.

Fish of the herring family, which are not easy to catch, make up nearly half of the world's fishing catch. The yearly total is 6,400 tons which shows us what a staggering number of fish must be involved.

Water forms about eighty per cent of the weight of a fish.

Vision is severely limited under water but hearing is increased.

Camouflage deceives fish in the same way as it deceives men.

Schools of fish are not only of one species but are also of roughly the same size and behave as a group again after being disturbed.

Some of the fish that eat food of the shellfish type are very noisy eaters and can be heard clearly under water.

Thousands of fish that live in the deepest and darkest waters light up their environment by being luminous.

There are more different kinds of fish (about 20,000) than any other creatures with backbones.

Sounds travel further in water than they do in air.

A large electric eel can give off shocks of the staggering size of 550 volts which can severely injure a man.

The fish which can deliver big discharges of electricity seem to use the gift mainly to stun their prey after which it can be eaten at leisure.

The herring fishermen of Ghana use special paddles with a three-pronged end like a tuning fork for listening to the movement of herring shoals. The paddle is put in carefully in a downwards direction and slowly turned round while the ear of the fisherman is kept glued to the end of the handle.

SURGEONFISH

BUTTERFLYFISH

ANGEL FISH

NEON TETRA

The sperm whale is a member of the toothed whale group

sporting facts

The pentathlon is a feature of the modern Olympic Games as it was in Ancient Greece

World Cup football

Association Football is now the most important sport in the world and the first Football League was composed of twelve teams which started to play each other in 1888. Now there are hundreds of leagues throughout the world and the recent tendency is for the great international clubs to move towards a Super League. This comes about every four years when the World Cup is played off. In 1966, England became holders of the World Cup when they beat West Germany 4-2 in the final at Wembley. This unexpected triumph was planned and carried through by that quiet but remarkable man, Sir Alf Ramsey who had foretold victory when it seemed impossible.

The Olympic Games

The Olympic Games in Ancient Greece started in 776 B.C. and continued every four years for centuries. Victory in the games was one of the highest honours in the Greek world. The games were revived on an international amateur basis in 1896, fittingly enough in Athens, and the great hope was that they would improve international understanding, which has hardly been the case. The United States have won three times as many medals as the next three countries in order of merit – Britain, Sweden and the U.S.S.R. The U.S.S.R. however, has only competed since the last war and will soon be in second place. The 1968 Games were held in Mexico, and Munich will be staging them in 1972.

Rugby

Football was a game first played in the Middle Ages in which hundreds of people took part. The ball was carried and the sport was more or less a running fight to which the possession of the ball gave some point. Modern Rugby is usually considered to have begun at Rugby's famous public school when William Webb Ellis ran with the ball in his arms, contrary to normal practice at that time. Blackheath was the first club to open about a century ago, and now rugby is a world sport.

A player scoring a try in a rugby match

IT'S A FACT!

The game of lacrosse was learned from the Red Indians in Canada.

Ice-yachting has been practised in the Netherlands on frozen inland water for about four hundred years.

Darts

This game was undoubtedly born in the English Inn and it remains a favourite amusement today. The first darts were home-made and flighted with feathers from fowls. Nowadays there is a wide selection from which to choose and the expert player has his own personal darts. The first dartboard was the end of a barrel but now a standardised board is used. The scoring numbers are arranged with high and low numbers next to each other so that poor players are penalised. In the centre is the bull's eye. On the outer edge is a narrow belt which doubles the scores and another belt halfway which trebles them. Play begins and ends with a double on the exact score.

Pelota

This game is played among the Basques, that strange and independent people who live in the Pyrenees area between France and Spain. Pelota is reputed to be the fastest game on foot in the world and has many different forms. It is played against an end wall in the manner of the English game of Fives with a similar lightning rebound and a similar fantastic demand upon the stamina of the players. In Rugby Fives the ball is struck with the hand but Eton Fives uses a bat and Pelota has two very similar forms. Unlike Fives, however, the scoring in Pelota follows the method used in Tennis. The game of Pelota can be played as singles, doubles or triples.

Players taking part in a game of pelota

Clay pigeon shooting

Clay pigeon shooting was, in the first place, a way of teaching the unskilled the difficult art of shooting game birds with a 12-bore shotgun. The clay "pigeons" look nothing like the birds whose name they bear; they are actually discs of clay, dished like a saucer, and about four inches across. When fired by a strong spring, however, the "pigeons" behave like birds in their erratic flight at about the right height and speed so that they test the sportsman's aim. Clay pigeon shooting has now developed into an independent sport.

A sportsman shooting at a clay pigeon

Geoff Hurst scoring for England in the 1966 World Cup final against West Germany

The marathon race in modern athletics has been fixed at 26 miles 385 yards.

There is no limit to the height of rugby goalposts, hence the saying, – "the higher the posts, the richer the club."

A Rugby League team has only 13 players compared with Rugby Union's 15. There are six forwards instead of eight.

A "duck" in cricket is when a batsman is dismissed without scoring.

Today glass marbles are called "alleys". Originally marbles were not made of clay but of real marble and the superior ones were made of alabaster, hence "alleys".

The "Ashes" for which Australia and England fight in international cricket were made by burning the stumps used in the first Test in England.

25

pomp and pageantry

Lord Mayor's Show

Each year in early November the Lord Mayor's procession through London heralds the new Lord Mayor. Leading his great coach comes a long cavalcade of decorated lorries and floats representing different trades and activities of the City of London. This yearly custom goes back, without a break, to the Middle Ages. In those days there was a guild for every craft and trade, and the mastermen and apprentices of each guild were keen rivals. On high days and holy days the guilds offered religious plays, the favourite day being Corpus Christi in June. The tradition of guild display remains in the Lord Mayor's Show.

The State Opening of Parliament

Russian Parades

Red Square in Moscow is the traditional place for the display of Soviet power and achievement. The square is dominated by old buildings which date from the Tsarist days: the Cathedral of St. Basil with its variegated "onion" towers; and the Kremlin, the great fortress of the Tsars. On special days, such as May Day or the Anniversary of the 1917 Revolution, spectacular displays are given by athletes from all over the Soviet Union, and the latest weapons of the Red Army trundle past leading Soviets on the rostrum. Solo achievements, like the late Yuri Gagarin's first space flight, are acclaimed officially in Red Square. It is the shop window of Russian propaganda – and the displays are always most impressive.

State Opening of Parliament

The State Opening of Parliament is performed by the Queen, the living representative of the age-old Crown of England and the most important link in the constitution. Although the Queen has no direct political power, everything is done in her name and nothing becomes law until she signs it. For the State Opening the Queen wears her Crown and regal robes and travels by the Irish State Coach. When the Queen reaches Westminster she is robed for the ceremony and ascends the throne in the House of Lords. The Commons are sent for to come to the Bar of the House, and the Lord Chancellor hands the Queen the speech which she reads to open the new session of Parliament.

Part of a splendid and colourful procession making its way through the streets of Siena to the traditional horse race

The Siena Horse Race

Siena is a hill town some 30 miles south of Florence in Italy. Perhaps more than any other Italian city it has remained the most medieval in appearance. If a man emerged from a doorway in full armour, probably no one would be the least surprised.

One of the major attractions is the horse race which is run every two years in the open space in the centre of the town where it is watched by a huge crowd of spectators – and of late has become one of Italy's biggest tourist attractions due to its colour and pageantry.

Each part of the city enters a horse, and the section owning the winner holds a triumphant banquet to which the victorious horse is invited to eat from a special manger. The whole occasion is gay with banners and colourful costumes of medieval days, of which the residents are justly proud.

Inauguration Day Parade in Washington

May Day Parade in Red Square, Moscow

The Edinburgh Tattoo

Tattoo originally described a type of drum-beat to recall billeted troops from the inns, but now it means a great military parade. The most famous tattoo is held on the Esplanade of Edinburgh by searchlight and floodlight. The Esplanade is an old parade ground, and with the castle as a backdrop, is a fitting stage for the display.

The Holy Blood: Bruges

The great processions of the Catholic Church are famed for their magnificence and impressive ritual. At the historic town of Bruges in Belgium a few drops of the blood of Christ are preserved in the Chapel of the Sacred Blood. Every year, on the first Monday in May, a procession of priests and dignitaries honour the shrine.

Royal Ascot

The race meeting at Ascot every summer is the leading social event of the British Turf, and there is fierce competition among the ladies to wear the most stunning dress and hat – which is all part of the fun. The Queen, by tradition, makes the Grand Drive down the course before the racing and the betting begin.

unusual transport

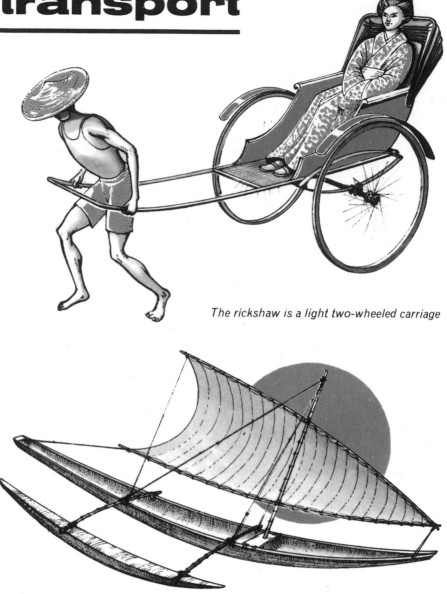

The rickshaw
The rickshaw is said to have been invented by a missionary in Japan and is, as its name means, a vehicle drawn by manpower. Although its use spread to India and South Africa, it is now becoming a curiosity and being replaced by the taxi. However, the very light two-wheeled carriage can be pulled by a rickshaw "boy" at a swift trot for long distances. A later form was a tricycle rickshaw, pedalled by its owner.

The hydraulic lift
At the seaside this old-fashioned type of lift carries visitors from the beach to the cliff top. There are two cars, each having a large tank underneath. The cars are connected by cables and pulleys, and as one descends the other is pulled up. The descending car has a full tank and the ascending car an empty one. Emptying and filling the tanks is the sole method of operation.

Outrigger canoe
This canoe is found in both the Pacific and Indian oceans and is an excellent idea for giving stability to a very light craft used for ocean travel. The outrigger is a log shaped to a point at both ends and lashed parallel to the canoe. Since the canoe always travels with the outrigger to windward, it must be shaped the same fore and aft for two-way travel. With a sail, 20 m.p.h. is possible in the Trade Winds.

The rickshaw is a light two-wheeled carriage

An outrigger canoe, made from a log which is pointed at both ends, in full sail

IT'S A FACT!

The traditional Chinese wheel-barrow has its wheel mounted in a slot in the middle of a platform like a tabletop. The goods are balanced all round and a very good weight can be carried.

The travelator at the Bank Underground Station in London is an escalator without steps. It is really a quickly-moving conveyor belt which carries thousands of passengers daily from one level to another.

The London Postal Service has its own tube railway joining some of the most important sorting offices under the streets of London.

Portering, the simplest method of transporting goods, is used in London markets today and surprising dead weights are carried on the head. The Billingsgate fish porters have a special hat to act as a base for the heavy boxes.

The first bicycle was a hobby horse. It had no pedals or driving mechanism. The rider sat astride and scooted on both sides with his feet on the ground.

In Okinawa, the local children who have to cross an estuary use stilts to go to school.

Gondolas of princely design are still used in Venice to conduct visitors through the narrow canals. The gondoliers use a single oar and often sing romantically as they work.

Monorail

The use of a monorail (a one-rail track) for trains has intrigued inventors and engineers from the earliest days of railways. Monorails are very suitable for high speeds and gradient climbing, but they present many problems in their construction. A monorail local railway operated in Ireland for nearly 40 years up until 1924. Now monorails have been revived in Germany and Japan, and are planned for other countries.

Cars travelling at high speed on a monorail

A highly manoeuvrable moon vehicle being tested in Northern Arizona

The moon car

Now that an unpiloted space rocket has made a soft landing on the surface of the moon, it is only a matter of time before astronauts venture on to the dusty surface themselves. Already engineers are working on essential equipment, and a prototype moon car has already been built. It has frame chassis of the "bedstead" type, and huge wheels with heavy tyres to cope with the moon's soft-dust surface.

All Arctic travel takes place on a two-runner sledge.

Sedan chairs, named after the town of their origin, were used in London in the 17th and 18th centuries. Each had two chairmen, one walking in front and one behind, who supported the chair on poles.

The Eskimo one-man canoe called a kayak is made of a light framework of wood covered with sealskin. It fits tightly at the waist and the Eskimos can use them in any weather.

The bicycle

One of Britain's oddest cycles was made in 1967. It is 30 feet long and is ridden by 14 riders. The first speed record of $15\frac{3}{4}$ miles in an hour was made on the famous "penny-farthing" cycle. Although it had a heavy steel frame and was dangerous to ride, the pedals working directly on to the big wheel gave it high, fast gearing.

This quatrodecimalopede was built for fourteen people and weighs $1\frac{1}{2}$ tons!

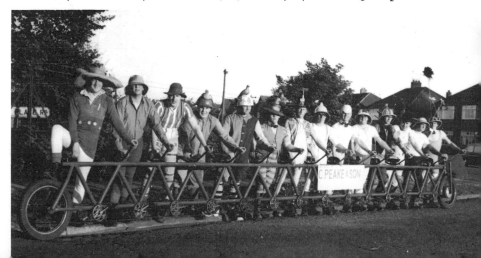

maps and symbols

Where would you expect to find kangaroos? In Australia, of course. And where would you expect to see tea growing? In China, of course. They were not very difficult; now test your knowledge with these. Below are the map outlines of six countries (not necessarily the right way up!) See if you can relate the pictures on the opposite page with the countries where you would expect to see them. (Answers on page 63).

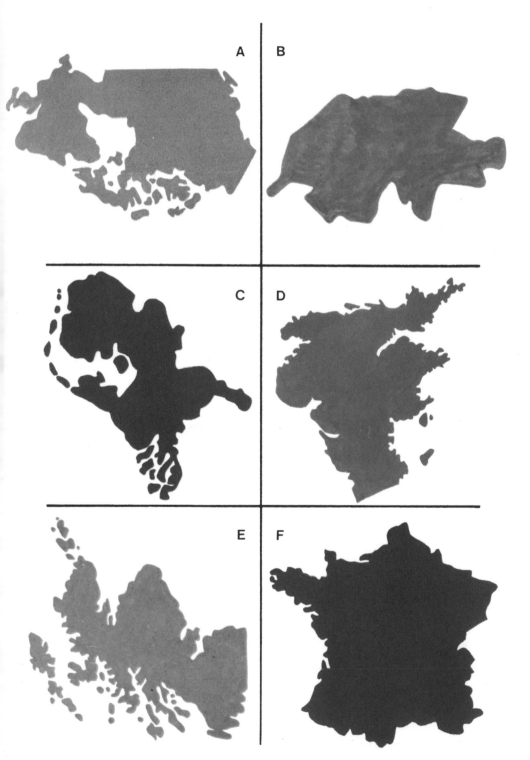

A

B

C

D

E

F

1

5

9

13

17

21

2

3

4

6

7

8

10

11

12

14

15

16

18

19

20

22

23

24

famous sayings

Beau Brummel making an insulting remark about the Prince Regent to his friends

Who's your fat friend? *Beau Brummel*

Beau Brummel was as famous for his foppish appearance as he was for his insolent outspokenness. By the outrageous use of both qualities he became the dictator of fashion in the time of the Regency and the intimate friend of the Prince Regent. The pleasure-loving prince had a great weakness for clothes and a sensitive awareness that he was too fat to be really smart. In order to insult the Prince Regent, at the time of a famous quarrel, Brummel spoke these words so that the prince could overhear them.

I have nothing to offer but blood, toil, tears and sweat, *Sir Winston Churchill*

These words were typical of Churchill's speeches at the blackest time of the Second World War. Britain's European allies were beaten, the outlook was bleak, but Churchill's stark honesty and resolution never to give in whatever happened exactly fitted the mood of the British people.

Thank you, madam, the agony is abated, *Lord Macaulay*

These words said to be spoken by the great historian when he was only a little boy, after scalding coffee had been spilt on him, are but one of the quotations often made to illustrate how precocious he was. Later it was said that he could read a page of a book, close it, and recite the page word for word from memory.

Coleridge talked on for ever; and you wished him to talk on, *Hazlitt on Coleridge*

The poet Coleridge was one of the best-read men in a highly educated society and accepted as the best talker of the day. It has been said that to hear Coleridge lecture on Shakespeare was like reading Shakespeare by flashes of lightning. People fought and used every trick to wangle an invitation to his famous Sunday afternoon tea parties where the spell-binding Coleridge held forth by the hour.

Germs have parents like men themselves, *Louis Pasteur*

Pasteur was a brilliant French chemist who started the serious study of bacteria. He made a long study of fermentation and found that bacteria could be controlled by heat treatment which has given the word "pasteurised" to our language in connection with milk.

Louis Pasteur studying bacteria

Absorbed in a mathematical problem, Archimedes was killed by a Roman soldier

Give me a firm spot on which to stand, and I will move the earth, *Archimedes*

These words were not a silly boast but the attempt of Archimedes to convey to his hearers how powerful was the use of levers which he had discovered. Archimedes was the greatest applied scientist of ancient times but his powers of concentration cost him his life. At the siege of Syracuse by the Romans, orders had been given to spare his life at all costs but the great man was so absorbed in a mathematical problem that an impatient Roman soldier who could get no word out of him, ran him through and killed him.

Oliver Cromwell, from a painting by Lely

Indeed I tremble for my country when I reflect that God is just, *Thomas Jefferson*

Thomas Jefferson was the third President of the United States and Secretary of State to Washington. He was the most talented of all the remarkable men who started the American Republic. Trained as a lawyer, he remained a scholar both classical and scientific all his life and was a brilliant linguist. He bought Louisiana from Napoleon, revised the laws and founded the university of his native Virginia, and did pioneer work on the monetary system, the freeing of slaves, and promoting education for all.

Let me smile with the wise, and feed with the rich, *Samuel Johnson*

Dr. Johnson was noted for his witty conversation and his love of good food. In Boswell's *Life of Johnson* are countless examples of the great man's amusing, argumentative and strongly worded observations on everything and everyone.

We are not interested in the possibilities of defeat, *Queen Victoria*

Queen Victoria was surrounded by a galaxy of great men and often her own remarks brought a smile to her hearers. She was, however, sometimes much nearer to the spirit of her people than they were. This comment became a slogan in the Second World War.

Mr. Lely I desire you would use all your skill to paint my picture truly like me, and not flatter me at all; but remark all these roughnesses, pimples, warts and everything as you see me, otherwise I will never pay a farthing for it, *Oliver Cromwell*

These were the instructions given by Cromwell, England's only dictator to his official artist. All the forthright bluntness and driving vigour of the man can be felt in these words and his contempt for outward show.

There ain't no way to find out why a snorer can't hear himself snore,
Mark Twain

Samuel L. Clemens was the real name of the author of *Tom Sawyer* and *Huckleberry Finn*. He was famous for his humour and down-to-earth qualities acquired in the pioneer world of the Mississippi. In early life he had been a pilot on the famous paddle steamers, and "by the mark, twain" was one of the pilot's calls. In later life he was surprised to find that the newspapers had announced his death and drily commented, "The report of my death was an exaggeration."

Many a good hanging prevents a bad marriage, *George Bernard Shaw*

Shaw loved to prod people with his biting wit and scandalise them with his novel ideas. He certainly succeeded in waking up the English theatre and making problem plays popular. He lived to be nearly a hundred and was both a vegetarian and a teetotaller.

Queen Victoria (1819-1901)

Other famous sayings

I like work; it fascinates me. I can sit and look at it for hours, *Jerome K. Jerome*. **Guns will make us powerful; butter will only make us fat,** *Goering* (who was very fat). **He who can does. He who cannot, teaches,** *Shaw*. **Liars ought to have good memories,** *Algernon Sidney*. **Had Cleopatra's nose been shorter, the whole history of the world would have been different,** *Pascal*. **I hate quotations,** *Emerson*.

Indians and prairie wagons

The Indian hunters were used to following their quarry wherever it led them and long before the English and French appeared, they had caught and tamed the wild horses which the Spanish had brought to America. Their famous trails, such as the Oregon and the Santa Fé, crossed the land from coast to coast and along these excellent trails came the pioneers with their goods loaded into covered wagons known as "prairie coasters". When the convoy halted for a while, the wagons were drawn up in a defensive ring against Indian attack.

The Baltimore and Ohio Railroad Company ran one of the first public services

The '49 gold rush

Land-hungry men and women kept the flow of new inhabitants moving steadily westwards but in 1849 the general advance turned into a stampede. News came of a gold strike in California and immediately a host of speculators raced to join the genuine prospectors who had made the strike. Soon the population of California swelled and the territory became a full state in 1850. Once the excitement had been tamed and the lawlessness had disappeared, people decided to stay in California partly because of the marvellous climate.

The iron horse

Some of Stephenson's engines were brought to Pennsylvania in the 1830's but only short stretches of line were laid. As the drive to the West gathered speed, it was the new steam paddle boats which made the Mississippi the main highway of America. The Civil War showed the value of the North's railway lines and when peace came, a start was made on the building of a transcontinental railway. The Union Pacific line was a fantastic task on which thousands of Irishmen and Chinese laboured. One construction party started eastwards from Sacramento in California and the other from Omaha in Nebraska, moved westwards to meet them. They raced towards each other and the golden spike which united the two halves was driven in on the 10th May, 1869, in Utah.

Open range or wire fences?

At first there was room for everyone in the great western wilderness and full liberty to earn a living in any law-abiding way. The first settlers were merely pirate farmers who reaped two or three quick crops and then moved westwards, leaving the exhausted ground behind them. But when the farmers settled more permanently, they ran wire round their holdings to act as boundaries and to keep out wandering cattle. Cattlemen were enraged at this interference with the open range and they often rooted up the wire and let the cattle run over the ploughland. Violent quarrels broke out between farmers and cattlemen with some loss of life and many films have been based on this period.

Eventually law and order was restored. Farmers settled on the richer prairie land permanently to grow their crops and raise sheep and the cattlemen moved further West and themselves settled down in ranches with enormous areas of land for their own use. At first cattle were driven to market in their thousands over hundreds of miles by drovers, but once the railway was established this picturesque event became unnecessary.

Indians attacking a wagon ring.

The buffalo

The Red Indians were a Stone Age people still living as hunters chasing animals across the boundless plains of the prairies. As the white men advanced the Indians were gradually crowded out of their old hunting grounds and naturally they fought back savagely. The great herds of buffalo were their life for from the buffalo they could obtain the food and leather which supplied them with almost all they needed. These buffalo were very dangerous to the new railways and thousands were killed. The Indians were now even worse off and their way of life became impossible.

Buffalo were hunted by Red Indians for food and clothing

One of the famous Colt revolvers

The gun duel

The lawlessness of the West has been glamorised by the cinema into a sporting contest between noble and brave gunmen. Recent research shows that this was not the case. Most of the notorious gunmen were violent criminals who ended their career with bullets in their backs. The struggle to bring law and order to the West was long and bitter. At first the gunmen and hired thugs were able to terrorise wide areas with little risk of receiving their just deserts, but as the number of respectable citizens increased, they were able to form effective posses to aid the sheriff in bringing villains to justice.

The civil war

The American Civil War (1861-5) ravaged pioneer America and the South never fully recovered from the disaster. Yet the two thorny questions under dispute, negro slavery and state independence, were correctly settled and the United States went forward even more surely afterwards. The South had all the advantages at first but gradually the industrial power of the North brought them inevitable victory.

A dispute between cowboys and farmers

child. en in boo ks

Alice with some of the characters from Lewis Carroll's immortal books

Alice in Wonderland

The Adventures of Alice in Wonderland is one of the most curious books in our language written by one of the oddest authors. Lewis Carroll, actually the Reverend Charles Lutwidge Dodgson, was a mathematics lecturer at Oxford for nearly thirty years and several textbooks on mathematics and logic stand to his credit. Carroll was a bachelor but he often told his stories to children, and Alice was a real child, the daughter of Canon Liddell, the famous Greek scholar.

The book exists on very many levels. Young children like the weird characters, the White Rabbit, the March Hare and the Cheshire Cat, but as we grow older the conversations grow two-edged and we find that there are subtle layers of humour deeper down and that we have met people remarkably like these odd characters in daily life. Carroll's humour specialises in situations which are obviously absurd but he goes on to treat them logically until we are not quite sure which world is crazy, his or ours.

IT'S A FACT!

Little Paul Dombey is born in *Dombey and Son* as his mother dies. The sickly boy cannot realise his father's ambitions and, far too wise for his years, foresees his own early death in the sound of the sea.

In *Oliver Twist,* Dickens drew attention to the callous treatment handed out to parish orphans in the name of charity.

***David Copperfield* has the same initials as Charles Dickens only they are reversed and this is doubtless intentional for there is much of Dickens' own life story in the book. Like Mr. Micawber, Dickens' father was imprisoned for debt when he was a boy.**

The humorous description of the fat boy, Joe, who cannot stop eating and is always falling asleep in *Pickwick Papers* is an accurate description of a boy suffering from a serious disease which was not understood at the time.

David Copperfield

Dickens suffered badly in his schooldays and in *Nicholas Nickleby* he pillories the evil school kept by Mr. Squeers at Do-the-boys Hall.

Dickens has created more memorable characters than any other English writer and many of these are unhappy children for whom the great author fought valiantly.

Becky Sharp

The main character of *Vanity Fair* is Becky Sharp who later becomes a dangerous scheming woman. The book opens with Becky leaving the Academy belonging to Miss Pinkerton who terrifies every girl. The parting battle between the arrogant, ignorant Headmistress and the rebellious sharp-tongued Becky is won by the cool young girl.

Tom Sawyer

Tom Sawyer, an orphan, and Huckleberry Finn, the son of the town drunk, are mischievous boys living on the Mississippi where their creator Samuel L. Clemens, or Mark Twain, was born in pioneer days. Mark Twain was a famous humorist and the two bad boys are described with laughing sympathy. Tom is always trying to get his escapades past the eagle eye of Aunt Polly with poor success but things are made worse by the treachery of his half-brother Sid, a good boy, who regularly betrays him. The crowning incident is when Tom and Huck run away and, believed to be drowned, creep back to watch their own funeral service.

Tom Brown's Schooldays

Tom Brown is a boy at Rugby, the famous public school, about a hundred years ago. The author, Thomas Hughes, had himself been at Rugby under the famous Dr. Arnold and the book reflects much of his own boyhood. Before Dr. Arnold the public schools had sunk very low but he raised their standards on the basis of clean living, hard work and sportsmanship. The story is designed to show how the system worked. Tom arrives at Rugby, a shy, nervous boy and undergoes his full share of bullying and persecution. But having had to work hard, play hard and fight hard for his rights Tom Brown toughens up and eventually becomes a self-confident boy.

Jim Hawkins

Jim Hawkins is the manly boy who is the hero of *Treasure Island*. His father is dying when the drunken old pirate comes to hide at their inn, the *Admiral Benbow*, and draws other members of Captain Flint's crew after him; vicious characters like Black Dog and Blind Pew, who are convincingly described. At Bristol, Jim meets Long John Silver and the *Hispaniola* and the great treasure hunt with all its adventures is on. Perhaps the most fascinating part of the story is Jim's relationship with the wicked and attractive Long John Silver who finally escapes single-handed, resolute to the last.

Tom Sawyer (top) the mischievous orphan, above, Tom Brown at Rugby School and left, Jim Hawkins with Long John Silver

Maggie Tulliver

Maggie and Tom Tulliver live in the Mill on the Floss and are finally drowned in the floods. Like a true brother and sister they quarrel fiercely but are really inseparable. Maggie is a tomboy with a fierce temper which covers a passionate nature. When life is too much for her she climbs to the attic of the mill and drives nails into an old wooden doll. Maggie is a self-portrait of George Eliot, whose real name was Mary Evans.

Little Women

This American story by Louisa M. Allcot describes the daily life of four sisters, Jo, Meg, Beth and Amy. The family have seen better days and, as their father is away at the wars, the four young girls cheerfully support their mother in keeping the home running. The four girls are very different. Meg at sixteen is the oldest sister and tactfully aware of her role as deputy mother while Jo is a clumsy rangy tomboy who intends to take her father's place and is always in scrapes. Of the younger girls, Beth is sweet but frail and nearly dies while mother is visiting their father, lying wounded in a military hospital. Amy, the youngest, is the prettiest and vain and has most trouble with her desire for beautiful things. The rich young boy next door, Laurie, and his young tutor provide the girls with romantic interest and the book ends with father safely returned and Meg engaged to be married.

Louisa M. Allcot's "Little Women"

37

the changing fortunes of war

The lord in his castle

After the break-up of the Roman Empire by the barbarians, there was little large-scale organisation again until the rise of nations led by kings. Meanwhile, men turned to local leaders for safety. The terrible Vikings raided the coasts and rivers of western Europe and a desperate need for safety caused the development of the fortified place. The first Norman forts, or keeps, were wooden but later castles were made of stone and became marvellously elaborate. Men were eager to belong to a lord in return for the real protection he could give and consequently the lord in his castle became the unquestioned ruler of his district. Once the raiders were overcome, however, the castle became the impregnable fortress of a lord who could dictate terms to his subjects. If the castle was built on solid rock or surrounded by a deep moat, not even mining could touch it and the only weapon was starvation, which could take many months. Thus the position of the lord was very strong.

Knights in armour competed against each other in jousting tournaments

Cavalry

From the time that the horse was first used in war, the mounted man had a supreme advantage when fighting against the man on foot, and there was no real change in this position until the coming of mechanised transport. Escape and pursuit were equally rapid for the horseman. Almost all the exceptional generals of the old days, like Alexander the Great, were gifted cavalry leaders. For a time, the magnificent quality of the Roman infantry, well-equipped and drilled in efficient tactics, made them able to subdue enemies that were technically inferior but once the barbarians were mounted, the later Roman army had to concentrate on cavalry. Until the coming of superior fire power, the Middle Ages was dominated by horsemen.

The knight in armour

Every gentleman in the Feudal Age was a fighting man by reason of his position. Consequently, he clothed himself in heavy defensive armour with as much care as he fortified his castle. Out of the saddle, the knight was clumsy and largely ineffective but once he was mounted on his armoured war charger, he was a lethal human tank that a man on foot could not be expected to face. For three centuries after the Battle of Hastings his power remained unchallenged. To keep in fighting practice and to satisfy the demands of medieval chivalry, knights jousted against each other in exciting tournaments, before the eyes of the court ladies.

Raiders attacking a medieval castle

The poor man and his bow

There were two ways to overcome the knight's supremacy; concerted action by a lot of men working together, or a new weapon of war which could adjust the balance. For a time the Swiss triumphed by the first method. By discipline, tactics and cold courage, they managed to organise their famous pikemen into a solid company which presented the knight with something like a huge porcupine to handle. The pikes were eighteen feet long. But this solution was capable of no further development.

The better solution was the use of a missile which could hit the knight before he reached close quarters. The first such effective missile was an English arrow fired by the famous longbow. At short range, the English longbow, handled by a village expert, could easily penetrate good armour. The best archers claimed that they could get three arrows travelling through the air at the same time so that the charging knights had to meet a hail of arrows. Regular competitive practice on the village greens gave the yeomen of England fantastic accuracy – and now the missile was in the hands of the common man who could defeat the knight.

The archer with his longbow won many battles for England

The broadside

By the end of the Middle Ages, firearms of various calibres had become a permanent feature of war. At sea the new colonising nations were foremost in adapting their ships to the new conditions and it was the English navy which devised the revolutionary broadside, entirely altering naval warfare. The basic idea was very simple. Previously, the guns on the decks of ships had to be small, otherwise they would roll the ship over. Now the Tudor naval architects thought of cutting a row of portholes in the side of the ship and mounting cannon behind them, low down in the vessel and near to the centre of gravity. In this way, much heavier guns could be fitted and the resulting wall of fire was capable of blasting an enemy ship out of the water, as the Spaniards found to their cost.

The Great Harry, *1514*

the changing fortunes of war continued

First World War soldier operating a Vickers machine gun

The first tank was used by the British in 1916

The machine gun

Once the Machine Age had arrived, mechanical methods were increasingly harnessed to war. In the 19th century the new rifles soon made mass formations of infantry and cavalry a thing of the past. Inventors then sought to provide a machine gun which could fire a continuous stream of bullets, but the first French and American guns to achieve this were too heavy. Hiram Maxim, an American, produced an effective gun, sometimes known as the Maxim and sometimes known as the Vickers. The ammunition itself worked the mechanism of the gun which could fire hundreds of bullets in a minute.

The tank

The first tank was used by the British Army in the First World War on the Somme in September, 1916. Its purpose was to straddle the trenches and to advance over uneven ground in order to attack and eliminate the machine gun nests which dominated infantry, who had to emerge from the trenches and thus expose themselves to enemy fire. The tank carried superior fire power and was protected by armour plate. Its tracks enabled it to lurch over very churned up ground. The first tanks spread terror among the Germans but otherwise were not very effective, but at Cambrai in 1917 a mass tank attack achieved a striking breakthrough at a cost which was cheap for that terrible war. But like the aeroplane, the tank was to see startling developments by the time of the Second World War. The Panzer divisions which Hitler prepared for his conquests soon showed that the tank had restored mobility and manoeuvre to modern war.

Air raids

The aeroplane knows no frontiers and the sky above is nowadays the front line for a people at war. Guernica, in Spain, was the first open town to be bombed but in the Second World War hundreds of industrial cities and their supply lines were smashed to prevent their oil, food and ammunition getting through to the armies. Ordinary people under severe bombing attack showed remarkable powers of survival but Hiroshima in 1945 showed that the atom bomb can destroy a city outright.

Fires from bombed buildings illuminating St. Paul's cathedral during the Blitz

Radar

The basis of radar is the sending of radio signals out into the atmosphere so that they strike an object and are thereby reflected back and picked up again by a receiver. The position of the object is then known and may be portrayed on a recording screen. The possibilities of using such apparatus to defeat surprise air attack was obvious. A research team of British scientists led by Watson-Watt worked on this idea from 1935 and Britain had "eyes which could see in the dark" when war inevitably came. As the war progressed the equipment became more and more effective and night fighters were guided on to raiding bombers by radar. Since the war, radar has been developed for peaceful ends, with remarkable success. Aircraft and ship navigation has been made easier and safer. Anti-collision watch can now be maintained by radar.

BEARING

DISTANCE

REVOLVING AERIAL

SPIRAL TIME BASE

4 3 2 1 0 1 2 3 4

Spot shows distance and bearing of plane from control tower

This diagram shows how radar plots the exact position of an aircraft

The submarine

Submarines are underwater craft whose job it is to sink enemy shipping. The Confederates were the first to use a submarine in anger in the American Civil War. Their submarines were hand-propelled and clumsy but they did achieve one success in sinking a warship, only for the submarine to be sucked down with its victim. Goubet, a Frenchman, built the first real submarine and other navies soon copied the French.

The invention of the Schnorkel tube by the Germans in 1944 enabled modern submarines to recharge their batteries while submerged and then in 1955 the Americans built the first atomic submarine. Also during the last war, midget submarines, handled by frogmen, were used to make surprise night attacks on ships.

IT'S A FACT!

During the last war the church bells of England were silenced by order so that they could be used as a warning if invasion occurred.

In his own day the fame of Leonardo da Vinci rested as much on his skill as a military engineer as on his artistic powers.

English surnames like Archer and Bowyer are obviously connected with the days of archery but Fletcher also means "arrow-maker".

Round towers were later added to castles because it was found that they resisted battering better than square ones.

Khaki, which means dusty, is the name for the drab type of uniform adopted by the British Army because the old bright redcoats became too good a target for the modern rifle.

The famous British Bren gun was produced at Enfield from a Czech model made at Brno. Bren is a combination of the first two letters of Brno and Enfield.

The main reason for Caesar's visits to Britain was to make a reconnaissance to establish how strong were the British tribes which had been sending help to their relatives, the Belgae, in their fight against his legions.

A submerged Polaris submarine discharging a long range guided missile

popular music

Jazz

Jazz came into being among the poor folk of the southern states of America, particularly in New Orleans. Negro spirituals, chain-gang and army songs all played their part but the robust, happy improvisation was driven on by a strong rhythmic beat. Little bands played in the tougher quarters, challenging sentimental ideas with this new exciting and emotional music. Jazz was condemned violently at first but nothing could stop the fanatical dedication of jazzmen to whom jazz was a way of life. Since then, many forms of jazz have grown up and jazz has acquired respectability. Jazz is now world-wide but so recent that musicians like Louis Armstrong and Duke Ellington have seen it all and are still playing.

Community singing

Group singing has certainly been popular on social occasions for many hundreds of years, for the old folk ballads provide choruses and refrains for the audience to come in with the singer. It is still a tradition with many people to sing the old songs when gathered together in the right party atmosphere, for the words are well known to everyone. A few years ago this natural, happy activity was taken up by sponsors and Community Singing was organised on a large scale in places where a good co-operative crowd could be expected. Brass bands were found to be excellent for open-air accompaniment. The crowning achievement of Community Singing was seen, and it survives, at the English F.A. Cup Final when over 100,000 people, mainly men, sing together before the match. The effect of the vast choir is intensely moving.

Brass band National Championships are held in England at the Albert Hall

Brass bands

Brass bands have a loyal and numerous following, particularly in the North and Midlands of England where small towns may have more than one excellent band. Collieries and large engineering works have encouraged their bands which have often won the National Championship. Brass bands are rightly so called because all the instruments except the percussion (drums) are made of brass. It is usual for the cornet to be preferred to the trumpet in these bands, for, although the two instruments have a similar range, the cornet is more flexible and has to cover all the lively passages normally played by the violins and the woodwind in an orchestra. The National Championship, which was held at the Crystal Palace before the big fire in 1936, now takes place at the Albert Hall.

Marie Lloyd singing at a music hall

Music hall

Music Hall was one of the gayer creations of the serious Victorian Age. There were Music Halls in all the big towns which gave variety shows of a free and easy type where the audience joined in heartily. The programme was not printed but the items were announced melodramatically by the Chairman who presided over the revels with a gavel in one hand and a drink in the other. Singing and dancing were the basis of the show and there were usually comedians, jugglers, acrobats and magicians. These shows began in the inns, and eating and drinking, as well as smoking, went on all the time and were even encouraged because they were an important part of the Music Hall's revenue. Proper plays were not allowed for they belonged to the serious theatre but character sketches were given which were vividly true to life. Performers like Little Tich, Marie Lloyd and George Robey were national heroes and their jokes and songs were on everyone's lips. The cinema destroyed the Music Hall but its material has been revived by television.

Street bands were a familiar sight in the poorer quarters of New Orleans where jazz was very popular

Pop singers and pop groups

In the last few years the pop singer and the pop group have swept all before them and brought fame and fortune to a number of young people who now have international names. The record companies are the main power in promoting this modern music and the other great beneficiaries, apart from the stars, are the makers of the guitar, the basic instrument of the new age. When Rock 'n' Roll and Skiffle came to England from America, popular music be-

came the property of the young amateur. Any group of young people could get together and hammer out a beat. Anyone who felt like it, could sing solo and tens of thousands tried and still go on trying. A few like Elvis Presley, Cliff Richard and the Shadows have stayed at the top ever since.

But the greatest sensation of this huge wave of young music-makers has been the Beatles. In one year from their first record, the Beatles reached the

Palladium, the Royal Variety Performance, and their first film. They played the country in one-night stands where the screams of the teenage audience almost blotted out their playing. The Mersey sound is said to have already made each of them a millionaire but the most striking thing is that they have remained themselves and kept their strongest group relationship and their likable personalities against all that publicity can do.

Beatles, John, Paul and George with Mia Farrow and Donovan, pose with the Maharishi during their visit to India

the human body

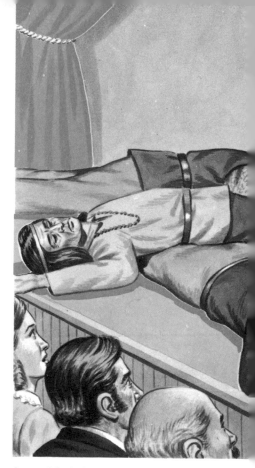
Samuel Colt demonstrating laughing gas

Laughing gas

Samuel Colt will always be remembered for his famous revolver, but he was also a man of many gifts and he used them to raise money for the promotion of his revolver during the mid 19th century. Colt had an interest in a Penny Museum in Cincinnati, Ohio, where he gave shows to the curious. One of the most successful was an exhibition in which he administered to himself and other people a dose of nitrous oxide, or "laughing gas." While under the influence of the gas the "performers" would caper wildly about the stage and generally act in an uninhibited manner which greatly delighted their rough-and-ready audience. To give a special show Colt hired six Red Indians to act as laughing-gas performers, thinking their capers would be even better. There was no time for rehearsal and he gave them the normal dose: they promptly went to sleep and remained unconscious for some time. A white man reacted in the usual way, for Colt did not know that the non-white races generally react more strongly to drugs and alcohol, and for him the show was a complete flop. But many who saw the show realised that the gas was a perfect anaesthetic and it was soon adopted by doctors and dentists. And thus it passed into medical practice throughout the world.

Doctor Edward Jenner giving James Phipps the first vaccination against smallpox

Surgery to the skull

Nowadays we are used to marvellous operations when surgeons can call on replacement organs and have ample time to work due to anaesthetics. Yet brain surgery was being carried out successfully in the Old Stone Age by men equipped only with flint knives. Skulls have been found which have been trepanned (large holes were cut in the skull and a section removed). New bone growth shows that some people survived the operation for years after. By trial and error the most sensitive parts of the brain were plotted out, and no doubt these early surgeons used some form of natural drug to make the operation possible.

The little milkmaid

Countrymen had long believed that those who caught cowpox were sure to escape the scourge of smallpox which ravished health and beauty up to the 19th century. It was Edward Jenner (1749-1823) who tested the belief and discovered vaccination. In May 1796 he examined Sarah Nelmes, a young dairymaid who had eruptions on her hand from cowpox. To test whether cowpox could ward off smallpox, Jenner took some matter from Sarah's hand and put it into the arm of a small boy, James Phipps. In July, Jenner transferred a smallpox infection to the boy, and repeated the transfer a few months later, but the boy was obviously protected by the vaccination and no harm resulted.

IT'S A FACT!

"A little of what you fancy does you good" is true because the digestive juices flow more readily when pleasure is expected by the body.

Every part of the body is renewed several times during the course of a normal life.

The blood pump

The heart is the most wonderful pump known to man. It is never serviced from the outside and it pumps away non-stop night and day from birth to death. In a lifetime of 65 years, it works continuously, beating 1,250 million times, driving the life-giving blood round the body. The blood is the supply line of the body and brings food and oxygen to every cell, and takes away the waste. So necessary is blood that even blood vessels have blood vessels. Everyone has enough of these tiny vessels to stretch twice round the world if they were placed end to end. The blood also contains the white corpuscles which are the body's natural defenders against disease. There are about ten pints of blood and plasma, which is mainly water, in the normal man.

The control mechanism

The nerves are the superb communication system which operates our body and mind. The brain and spinal cord form the main channel from which branches out a complicated network. The neuron, the basic cell of the nervous system, has delicate hair-like extensions which transmit an impulse across a tiny gap to the next neuron and, in this way, the whole body is a relay system. From the skin, eyes, nose, ears and mouth, signals are relayed back to the brain and orders are transmitted back. Some of the nerve fibres are coated with a special conductor which gives them even faster transmission. The nerves connecting with the lower part of the brain's core deal with automatic operations such as breathing; those connecting with the centre deal with mechanical actions such as walking; and those of the highest part with perception, pleasure and pain.

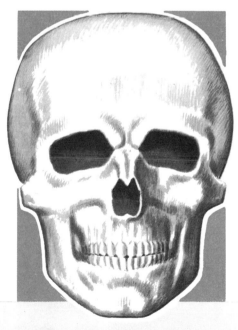

The human skull

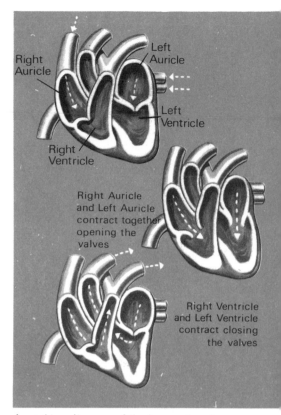

A working diagram of the human heart

Right Auricle

Left Auricle

Left Ventricle

Right Ventricle

Right Auricle and Left Auricle contract together opening the valves

Right Ventricle and Left Ventricle contract closing the valves

Food

Food is the fuel of the body and must be supplied regularly. It does not fall down through the digestive system but is moved along steadily by a churning action of the muscles. The stomach is a bag which enlarges when a heavy meal arrives in a softened condition. Here the incredibly complicated chemistry of the body begins and goes on in the intestines to break down the food into what the body requires, and to expel the waste. The liver is the key organ in the body's chemistry, building up new substances from the raw materials of the food, and feeding them to the blood stream for distribution to the countless cells of the body.

Noses were altered to increase their beauty in Ancient India.

Egypt had women doctors 2,000 years before Christ.

The Chinese have a tradition by which a fee is paid to the doctor when they are well but it is suspended when they fall sick until they are cured.

A flea which breeds on rats was the carrier of the Black Death which killed off half Europe in the Middle Ages.

The commercial value of the water and chemicals which make up the human body would only be worth a few coppers.

The largest solid organ is the liver.

If the endless messages sent and received by the brain had to be handled by electronic equipment, an enormous building would be required instead of the tiny area inside the human skull.

Cancer is not one sickness but has many very different forms. It arises from cells which are not weak but very aggressive. They break away from the body's system and set up on their own.

working animals

Horses and herdsmen

In the lands of America and Australia, vast herds of cattle and flocks of sheep are controlled by men mounted on horseback. In America, their mounts have often been broken in and trained from wild horses but all these horses were originally imported from Europe by the early colonists. Some of them later escaped and ran wild. In the prairies of North America, the cowboy is a fast disappearing figure and the exciting old days only live again at the professional rodeos. The outback of Australia also has a dwindling need for horses but on the pampas of Argentina riders work in the old way. These men are called gauchos and are even tougher and more hard-bitten than the northern cowboys. Everywhere, as mechanisation spreads round the world, the horse is giving way to the tractor and the jeep and it is only the primitive peoples who keep to the old ways.

Indian water buffalo ploughing rice fields

The camel

The camel is one of the most useful working animals and also one of the most unlovable. It is bad-tempered and can be very vicious but in desert areas it has no equal, for the camel can carry heavy loads for long distances across blistering desert. These large, ungainly animals have a peculiar swaying movement caused by both legs on one side moving forward together. Special adaptations make life in the desert possible for the camel. He has a stomach which can retain water and a special hump of fat which breaks down into food and water when the going is hard. Arabian camels have one hump and Bactrian camels have two and are even tougher. Apart from transport, camels provide the Arabs with meat, milk and raw materials for weaving. Just as with horses, there are heavy draught camels and finer swift-riding camels. All have to be five years old before they can work properly but, once mature, they can give service for many years.

Elephants

Elephants were used extensively in the teak forests of Burma by English timber companies before the last war. The Burmese, who can recognise the footprints of their own elephant, train the animals and, since an elephant lives about as long as a man, the natives often spend their entire lives with the same beast. These massive creatures are very strong. Roughly trimmed teak logs, which can weigh up to four tons, are dragged by these elephants over muddy ground and broken vegetation. The elephant is said to have a sense of humour and when the siren goes at the end of the day, the elephant downs tools just like the men.

Cowboys using horses to round up their cattle on the South American pampas

Carrier pigeons

For thousands of years, men have known about the carrier pigeon's fantastic homing instinct and its high-speed flight. To fasten a written message to the bird's leg is simple and the weight is negligible so that this method of communication is excellent. The Greeks and Romans used them both in peace and war but the most staggering example was in the Franco-Prussian War when a great number of carrier pigeons were flown in a balloon out of besieged Paris. Over a million letters were flown back into the city by this method. The Meyers, who founded the great banking house of Rothschild, used pigeons and so did Reuters, the international news agency. Radio and telephones have made the pigeon unnecessary today but pigeons are a valuable standby when mechanical and electrical devices fail.

The water buffalo

The Indian water buffalo belongs to the same family as the ox and is used for the same agricultural work. He is, however, bigger and stronger and has very large horns on his head which he carries very low. His special feature is his love of water and he will gladly rest in it up to his neck. His strength and his willingness to work in water make him an excellent draught animal for ploughing the rice fields because valley rice is flooded for the greater part of the growing season.

Sheepdogs

In the hilly parts of Great Britain, it is fascinating to watch the sheepdogs rounding up the flocks. From the distance at which the shepherd works, the dog can often scarcely be seen but the scattered white dots, which are sheep, suddenly begin to draw together and then form a white mass which turns and flows in obedience to the whistles and arm signals of the shepherd. At the National Sheepdog Trials, the top dogs can be seen selecting and manoeuvring single sheep into pens.

Guide dogs for the blind

There are now over 1,000 blind owners of guide dogs in this country, provided by the Guide Dogs for the Blind Association of Great Britain. The idea of guide dogs began accidentally in Germany when a blinded soldier was taken safely along a hospital path by an Alsatian he had been asked to hold. An American couple living in Switzerland heard of this and took the idea up in their kennels. Later, the first owner of a guide dog travelled from Tennessee to be trained. After weeks of patient training, the dog was able to guide its master safely across busy roads. Soon, the owner and his dog returned to the United States. Their arrival back in New York caused a sensation which led to the "Seeing Eye" dog organisation being founded in the United States in 1932. The British organisation followed and now has three centres in England and one in Scotland. Every dog picked for training is first closely examined to ensure that it is suitable for this specialised type of work. The training of a guide dog is very intensive and usually takes about four months to complete at a cost of around £250.

A guide dog leading his blind master

A chain of donkeys in the Middle East carrying heavy loads

47

this man was great

The father of electricity

Modern man controls his universe at the touch of a switch and the power he uses is electricity. All this has become possible because Michael Faraday invented an electric motor and an electric dynamo. There were many scientists interested in electricity and its curious powers at the time and Faraday met Volta and Ampère when he was travelling abroad as a young man with Sir Humphrey Davy. But Faraday had an instinct for the practical application and a genius for making apparatus. His faith in his own findings was so great that he often risked his life experimentally to prove his marvellous ideas, of which Einstein has said that we have only learnt half of what we can from Faraday.

A photograph of Faraday taken in 1855

Faraday lecturing Prince Albert and the royal children

The poor boy

Michael Faraday was born in London in 1791 to very poor parents. Despite crushing poverty the Faradays were very godly and extraordinarily cheerful but it did mean that Michael received little education, although he was always asking questions. At thirteen he was apprenticed to a bookbinder who handled newspapers (a luxury then) and rare books. One of the first books which Michael read was about chemistry. In his bedroom he made simple apparatus to test what the books told him and thus the pattern of his future life was formed.

Electric motor and dynamo

In 1821, Faraday managed to spin a little wire round an upright magnet in a dish of mercury; that rotary movement could be produced by an electric current had been proved and Faraday had discovered the motor. In 1831, Faraday spun a large copper disc between the arms of a horseshoe magnet which recorded a continuous flow of electric current in a galvanometer. This simple experiment was the world's first dynamo.

Faraday's electric dynamo (1831)

Trinity House and the lighthouses

Faraday's services were in demand from the whole of England because of his practical success in solving scientific problems. Although his standard of living constantly improved, he was not very interested in money despite the persuasions of industry. However, he helped Trinity House with their care of Britain's lighthouses and held the position of scientific adviser to them for thirty years. During this time his travelling and visits to the coast probably helped to keep the health of this great man who overworked himself.

Faraday was dissatisfied with the old smoky oil lamps which had to be used in the lighthouses. He improved them until before his death he had the satisfaction of seeing them operated by electricity. Not only the mechanics interested him but the lives of the men who had to operate them. Finding that they were badly troubled with fumes, he realised that fresh air must be supplied and invented a ventilation system. All these new ideas were tested in a single lighthouse for efficiency before Faraday would allow them to be built into others.

Lecturing to the royal children

One day in February 1812, Faraday received a free ticket to hear the great Humphrey Davy lecture at the Royal Institution. He made notes of everything and later added drawings. A year later, recommended by his own superb notes, Faraday became laboratory assistant in the Royal Institution and worked with Davy. Sir Humphrey was brilliant but pleasure-loving and careless whereas Faraday had endless patience and dogged determination. Faraday lived in at the Institution and there, by permission he brought his bride, Sarah. But, after Davy's early death, Faraday gradually succeeded to his fame and position, finally becoming Professor of Chemistry.

Unfortunately the Faradays had no children and so Faraday decided to start special Christmas lectures for children at the Royal Institution. In 1855 Prince Albert paid him the tribute of bringing some of the royal children to hear his Christmas lectures.

IT'S A FACT!

The architects who constructed the Reading Room for the British Museum consulted Faraday on the problem of building the dome.

When asked what was his greatest discovery, Sir Humphrey Davy replied, "Michael Faraday".

The great painter J.M.W. Turner came to Faraday to give him help with fixing the pigments for his colours.

Faraday's great electric magnet

Faraday realised that atoms must have smaller electric parts, thus anticipating our nuclear understanding of the atom.

Faraday realised the need for a proper set of terms if electricity was to be adequately discussed. So he used the terms, electrode, electrolyte, anode, cathode, etc. which have stayed ever since.

Faraday did the groundwork for the electric motor and dynamo, and the transformer and condenser as well.

Benzene was discovered by Faraday from which an enormous by-product industry of dyes and perfumes has been developed.

Faraday, who was trained as a chemist, liquefied gases and thus made refrigeration possible.

As a personal experiment, Faraday produced a stainless steel. No one was very interested so he only made six razors with it and presented them to his friends.

Faraday made many alloys, including aluminium, and some new forms of heavy glass.

Radio, radar, and x-rays are heavily indebted to Faraday's work.

Faraday invented the foam used in fire extinguishers.

Faraday was a blacksmith's son and made nearly all his apparatus himself.

Faraday was one of the first to give forensic evidence in court.

inventions that changed our lives

William Caxton's printing press and a modern high-speed rotary newspaper press

Radio

The discovery of radio was based on the work of a host of practical and theoretical men. Clerk Maxwell (1831-79), for example, discovered the truth about electro-magnetic waves by pure mathematics, without the use of apparatus.

Marconi came to England in 1896 at the age of 22 and began the brilliant experimental work which enabled him to connect Cornwall with New-foundland by wireless signals in 1901. Since the world is round, scientists were puzzled as to why signals did not just fly off into space but then they found there are layers in the atmosphere that "reflect" the waves back to earth. Today satellites are used to bounce these waves back to earth artificially and thus television pictures can be sent round the world on the same principle.

A camera captures the moment of impact as a lump of sugar drops into a cup of tea

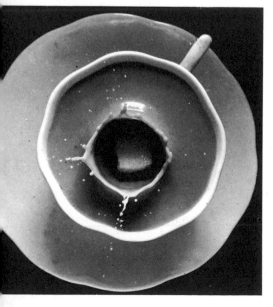

Photography

Photography is a method of making in-stant pictures and basically its prin-ciples remain constant. Improvements are always being made but perhaps the greatest single advance was the inven-tion of celluloid film, by Eastman, which made the film industry possible. Education has become strongly visual and modern man is taught by pictures as much as by the printed word. Hund-reds of documents can be recorded on one strip of microfilm and the Airgraph letters used in wartime, were recorded by the thousand on 16mm. film. Photo-graphy can record the slow growth of a plant or decide the winner in a race and it can record a lightning flash, or the feeble light of a distant star, with equal ease.

Television

Television has only been available to the general public in the most advanced countries since the Second World War. In Britain the viewing hours are limited but in America, children can watch television while they eat break-fast. Television combines the power of radio and film, for it takes place person to person as does radio, and it has made every home a cinema. When the television breaks down, we realise what a hold it has on our lives. Public figures now have to have a good tele-vision personality and they are thus trained for their appearances. The test is severe, for television misses nothing. So powerful is television in persuading people to buy what the advertiser recommends, that very high rates are charged for a minute's use of its time and extremely expensive programmes can be hired to attract viewers. The power of television can scarcely be measured.

Telephone

The first seven words heard over the telephone wire were: "Mr. Watson, come here! I want you!" Watson, Alexander Graham Bell's assistant, was in the basement of a house and the message came from the attic where Bell was transmitting. The telephone has improved but its principles have never changed. Today the whole world is linked by telephone and immediate communication is exceptionally easy. The only casualty of this new invention is the now dead art of letter-writing.

50

Sir Francis Chichester using radio at sea

Film

When men were able to use the camera for moving pictures, a form of art was born which was the special creation of our century. The exciting chase and knockabout comedy were the first triumphs and soon the great historic epics grew ever more spectacular. In 1927 the first talkie film emerged and revolutionised the industry. The world audience was catered for by cinemas built in every country but it is now being cut back by cinema's offshoot, television. However, colour has been added and now every event of any interest, personal or international, can easily be recorded on film. It is a universal eye. The first films were produced entirely in studios and the surrounding countryside but now location work takes camera teams everywhere, including the front line of a war. As time passes, film records are able to show us the historical events of this century as they actually happened.

Newspapers

Before the coming of radio and television, newspapers had undisputed sway as the main source of information and the power to influence people. The first newspaper which could be called a "daily" appeared in the early eighteenth century. A heavy tax was soon put on newspapers which lasted for 150 years so that they were only available to the well-to-do. Others, however, often paid a fee for a quick "read" of the paper in the famous coffee houses.

Although newspapers are now growing more alike, they can still be divided easily into those which aim at quality and those which aim at popularity. There are interesting reasons for this. Sunday papers were opposed as ungodly for a long time. The papers which did appear were weekday papers written for an educated class with plenty of leisure. When the tax came off, the working class, now receiving free education, bought papers at the weekend when they had time to read. These Sunday papers were more sensationally presented and this tradition has remained.

In 1896, Harmsworth began the *Daily Mail* at the cost of one halfpenny and it became the first newspaper to reach a million copy sale. British newspapers have easily the largest circulations in the world because one paper can cover the whole population in our tiny country. Where the distances are greater, the news becomes out-of-date.

Inside a studio a cameraman films a scene from a play to be shown on television

inventions that changed our lives *continued*

Nuclear energy

The explosion of two atomic bombs in 1945 demonstrated the enormous power which science could release by nuclear fission. The occasion of this success was dismally sad and, naturally, the scientists soon turned their attention towards using this gigantic force for peaceful ends. Men have dreamed for years of harnessing the tides and using the power of the sun, but here is a third natural power over which they have gained some control. The idea of nuclear power stations was soon put forward and eventually atomic reactors were set up to unlock nuclear energy. The task is both technical and difficult. Conventional fuels set up their own chain reaction once they begin to burn, but nuclear reaction is not automatic: breakdown must be contrived by artificial means. But the power available is worth all the trouble: a quantity of uranium will yield a million times more energy than an equal quantity of coal. Nuclear power presents no problem of bulk, for a sufficient quantity of uranium can be flown by one aeroplane to where it is wanted; whereas coal and oil need vast transport facilities. Atomic energy is becoming more and more the power of the future.

An early Peugeot

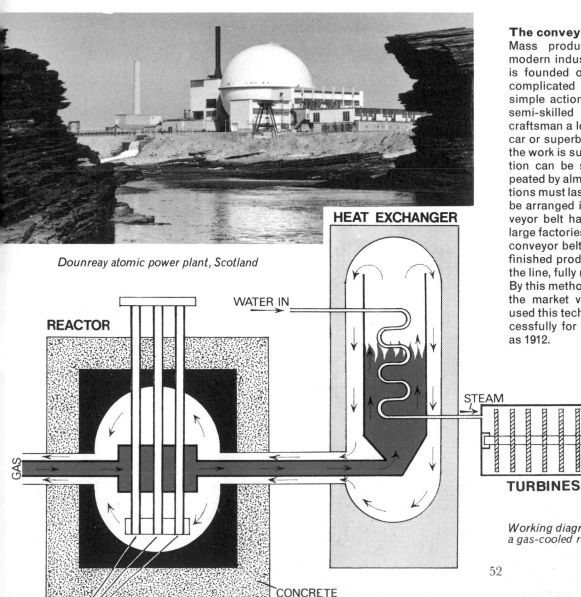

Dounreay atomic power plant, Scotland

The conveyor belt

Mass production is the secret of modern industrial development, and it is founded on the breaking down of complicated tasks into numerous simple actions which can be done by semi-skilled workers. It takes a fine craftsman a long time to make a racing car or superb cabinet by himself, but if the work is sub-divided, a single operation can be swiftly and efficiently repeated by almost anyone. These operations must last about the same time and be arranged in logical order. The conveyor belt has made this possible. In large factories and with large staffs, the conveyor belt comes into its own – the finished product coming off the end of the line, fully made, in a very short time. By this method articles can be put on to the market very cheaply. Henry Ford used this technique in Detroit very successfully for making cars as long ago as 1912.

HEAT EXCHANGER

WATER IN

REACTOR

GAS

STEAM

GENERATORS

TURBINES

Working diagram of a gas-cooled reactor

ELECTRICITY / POWER LINES TO GRID

CONCRETE

URANIUM RODS (heating circulating gas)

Motor cars

The motor car has become a popular status symbol in the industrial countries of today, and its fantastic multiplication is choking most large cities with jams and fumes. The first cars of the mechanised age appeared at the end of the 19th century and were really horseless carriages fitted with the new internal combustion engine. They were elegant toys of well-to-do sportsmen. It was the vision of Henry Ford, an American farm boy, who changed the world's attitude towards the car. A practical mechanic, Ford realised how useful personal transport would be if it could be made cheap enough. So he set about building a cheap but strong car which would have a serviceable life of five years and then be replaced by another. Everyone today views his car in this way. Ford was an assembly man. Whenever possible he got other people to make tyres or parts, while he concentrated on conveyor-belt methods of assembly. He also started a cheap spare-part service so that every man could be his own mechanic. His T-model, the famous "Tin Lizzie", was the first of the people's cars which other manufacturers, such as Austin and Volkswagen, have followed with great success.

Traffic jams are a familiar sight in cities

Advertising

The modern city-dweller is rarely ever out of the reach of the sight or sound of advertising ... from the humble postcard in the newsagent's window to the lavish TV show paid for by sponsors. Millions of pounds are spent on advertising in the United Kingdom every year, and the United States spends even more. Aeroplanes have been used to "write" slogans in the sky, and every serious and funny device supports the claim that "all the wise advertise". The advertiser must create a market for the producer. But nowadays the advertiser must work even harder to influence huge TV audiences which get wiser to his tricks, for he must win their confidence to make a true impact. And he must do so to make possible the mass-production which alone can repay the enormous production costs of modern industry today. Advertising has been called a "necessary evil", for our prosperity depends upon it.

Refrigeration

Once oranges were seen only at Christmas, and perishable foods could be brought safely only over short distances. Consequently the food in our larders was rather monotonous. But about 100 years ago refrigeration was made efficient, and ships were able to deliver fresh foodstuffs from country to country. Today most homes have small refrigerators which can keep food fresh for days.

This drawing shows the pilot's view of the runway from the cockpit of an airliner

Aircraft

Above all other achievements in our century must be placed the development of the aeroplane which, in 60 years, has progressed from a crazy contraption of twine and canvas to a sleek projectile capable of fantastic speeds at high altitudes. In four runs on 17th December, 1903, Wilbur and Orville Wright each made two flights with a heavier-than-air machine. By 1909 Louis Blériot had flown the English Channel to indicate how easily the aeroplane could break the barriers of national frontiers. The Wrights' plane was a biplane, but Blériot's was a monoplane, which sparked off a great controversy about the merits of the two and which the monoplane later won. During the Second World War, Whittle designed a jet-plane and the Germans a jet bomb – inventions which now govern aircraft engine design. Today the United States has flown a jet-plane at over 2,000 m.p.h. The Comet was the first 500 m.p.h. airliner but the Concorde is expected to exceed 1,300 m.p.h.

unusual customs

Young swans being rounded up for the traditional custom of swan-upping

Swan-upping

The magnificent swans of England were once wholly owned by royalty, no private person being allowed to own them. Those on the Upper Thames are still the joint property of the Crown and the Livery Company of Dyers and Vintners of London, and are cared for after the old traditions. Every July, the young swans are rounded up for marking. This process is known as swan-upping. The beaks of the young birds are nicked with a penknife to a design which is their owner's brand mark. Broods belong traditionally to their parents' owner.

The Christmas tree

Christmas as we know it unites all sorts of traditions – Christian, Roman and Nordic. Most of the customs to do with trees, holly and mistletoe are Pagan in origin. The Christmas tree is a very recent addition to the British Christmas scene. It was introduced only a hundred years ago by Prince Albert, the Consort of Queen Victoria. The Germans call the Christmas tree "Tannenbaum" and they have a famous carol of that name. The Christmas tree, then, has no connection with the Christian story and belongs to the dark Nature worship of the northern pine forests.

The Christmas tree in Trafalgar Square, London

Cypriot wedding

A most interesting custom of a Cypriot wedding in both Greek and Turkish communities in Cyprus, is the pinning of money to the bride's dress by the guests invited to the wedding ceremony. These used to be pound notes but nowadays, they tend to be five-pound notes. This is the Cypriot way of making wedding gifts, as normal gifts as we know them, are not given. The sum total of all these notes is considerable and, of course, the money can be spent in any way the young people desire.

Pearly kings and queens

The Pearly Kings and Queens are a part of the festive life of Cockney London and can be seen at the important Bank Holiday fairs. In olden days, all the costermongers used to turn out in these flamboyant clothes, but now very few remain. The queen wears a huge black picture hat decorated with ostrich plumes. The king keeps to a well-worn cap but massed designs of pearl buttons and sequins cover the whole costume. The chief surviving family today is the Marriotts and the main aim of maintaining the old tradition is to collect for charity.

Tattooing

This ancient practice occurs all over the East, although the most impressive and exquisitely designed tattoos are seen on the Maoris of New Zealand. The designs are made by pricking the human skin. Colouring matter of some sort is then rubbed into the puncture. The small hole soon scars over and the colour is trapped permanently under the skin. Today, an electric needle is used which makes the operation much quicker. Tattooing was brought to this country mainly by sailors and servicemen.

Pearly King and Queen

54

IT'S A FACT!

The Dunmow Flitch (of bacon) is still awarded to a loving couple who will publicly declare that they have never wished themselves single again since their marriage. Chaucer mentions the custom in the *Canterbury Tales*.

In the days of busy horse traffic over cobbled streets, deep straw was frequently laid down outside the houses of the sick to deaden the noise of hooves and carriages.

Beating the Bounds is still a parish custom. In the old days, the children were beaten at all the boundary marks so that they would remember them but now the marks are beaten instead. In London, the choirboys have to take to the water in order to beat the boundary crossing the Thames.

Maoris do not kiss but rub noses when they wish to greet each other.

On the previous evening or on the actual day, the Yeomen of the Guard make a thorough search of the cellars of the Houses of Parliament in order to assure Parliament that no repetition of Guy Fawkes's Gunpowder Plot is about to take place.

Mint sauce is said to have been originally a dressing of bitter herbs to remind the Christian of the sufferings of Christ, the true Lamb.

The red and white pole still seen outside some barbers' shops dates from the time when they also bled people in the eighteenth century as a surgical service.

Many are the capers on Pancake Day. At Olney in Buckinghamshire, the housewives have an annual pancake race with their frying-pans in their hands while in Westminster School the boys scramble for a tossed pancake and the winner with the largest piece receives a guinea.

The great passion play

Oberammergau is the name of a beautiful Alpine village in Bavaria in Germany which is world famous for its Passion Play. The play is staged every tenth year and dozens of the villagers take part. Christ, His disciples and the Holy Women are all played by villagers who rehearse their great production very thoroughly and show it magnificently. Linked with the tourist industry, it has now become big business and seats are booked far ahead from abroad in the fine large theatre which has been built solely to house this production. About three hundred years ago, plague was rife in Bavaria with tragic loss of life but the village of Oberammergau was spared and in thankfulness to God, an act of worship was proposed. The villagers decided to enact the Passion of Christ as nearly as possible to the actual crucifixion and consequently, the performance takes several hours to complete. This deeply moving spectacle still continues and there is tremendous competition to play Christ, and the villager-actor chosen, grows his beard and hair long for the part. The village is also famous for its school of woodcarving.

Maundy money

Today the ceremony of giving the Maundy Money to the poor, takes place in Westminster Abbey on Maundy Thursday, the day before Good Friday. There are four types of small silver coins, of 1d., 2d., 3d., and 4d., in value, especially minted for this occasion. They have no milled edges but can be legally spent although they are more valuable as a collector's item. Once upon a time, the reigning king had to wash the feet of as many poor people as the number of years the monarch had lived and then give them money, food and clothing. James II was the last king to carry out the true ceremony.

The beautiful Alpine village of Oberammergau where the Passion Play takes place

55

strange substances

The pearl

Since men have always eaten shellfish, they long ago discovered the pearls lying in the pearl-oyster and pearl-mussel. Today they are mainly obtained from the pearl fisheries of the Persian Gulf. The true pearl is an abnormal growth in those oysters where it occurs. Something irritates the oyster, a piece of grit, or a grain of sand, and his body begins to direct some of the shell-forming cells to covering the foreign matter which has entered the surface of his body. Layer after layer of material is added and thus the pearl grows. In cultured pearls, the Japanese have learnt to insert a bead artificially into the oysters' bodies without killing them. Then they are suspended in wire baskets under rafts for a few years to add a true pearl covering. The longer they stay, the deeper the covering. Artificial pearls are simply glass beads with a special coating.

Amber

Amber fascinated the ancients by its beauty and its electrical properties. It is really a fossilised form of pine tree resin as may be seen from the fossilised insects in it which were once trapped by the sticky gum. It is yellow-brown in colour and almost transparent, giving a warm glow to the beads and cigar holders for which it is traditionally used. The Greek name for amber is "elektron" and static electricity can be generated in amber by rubbing.

Rubber

Rubber is Nature's own plastic and it is only very recently that it has been surpassed by synthetic rivals. It is made from a milky fluid called latex which is found under the bark of some tropical trees. In the raw state, it is very tough and seen as the crêpe on the soles of shoes. Some scientists think latex protects the trees from boring insects. For man, it is waterproof and also excellent for insulating electrical wiring. Having been vulcanised, it can be used for heavy duty.

A pearl lying in a pearl-oyster

Children on holiday at the seaside enjoying sticks of lettered rock

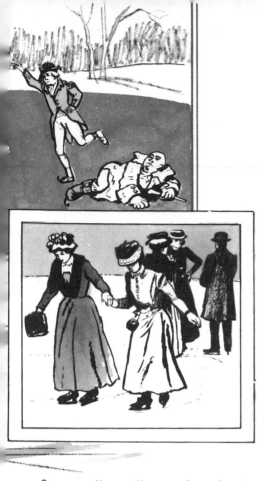

Some sporting pastimes performed on ice

Water

Water is plentiful enough, for over two thirds of the world's surface is covered by it and our bodies are more than ninety per cent water. Yet this liquid, in which life began on our planet, is very strange. It almost seems to reject a distinct personality for all its properties are rather negative. It has neither taste nor smell and is almost colourless. On chemical test, it shows neither acid nor alkali reaction but remains neutral. It conducts heat poorly but unlike most liquids, when frozen, it expands so powerfully that it can wreck steel bridges.

Lettering in rock

Every child is fascinated by seaside rock which always has the name of the resort – be it Blackpool, Brighton or Skegness – running right through it from end to end. Although the rock is sucked away, the name remains. How do the letters get inside? Obviously, they are put in when the rock itself is made. The original stick is as large as a tree trunk and the long strips forming the letters are large at first. The warm "stick" is then rolled and rolled until it comes down to normal sizes, the letters remaining true as the rock fines down.

Coral reefs

Coral is formed from the tiny skeletons of very simple animals and plants. New growths form on the old by a process known as budding, and so the great reef structures are built up from the tiny little deposits of limestone. The largest coral reef in the world is the Great Barrier Reef of Australia which is over a thousand miles long.

Mercury

Mercury, one of the oldest known metals, is also known by the descriptive name of quicksilver. It is the only metal which is a fluid at all temperatures and is therefore used in thermometers and weather instruments. Mercury does not moisten what it touches and it is one of the heaviest metals, being about 14 times heavier than water.

IT'S A FACT!

Glass-making was learnt accidentally by the Ancient World when casting in sand. The knowledge was lost in the Middle Ages and the art had to be re-discovered.

A catalyst is a substance which assists chemical change between other substances without suffering the least chemical change itself in the process.

Cochineal, the bright red colouring matter used in foodstuffs and cosmetics, comes from the dried bodies of the insect of the same name which lives on cacti in sub-tropical lands.

Beautiful music is drawn from a violin but the strings are made from the intestines of sheep and the hairs of the bow come from a horse's tail.

Like soot and coal, the diamond is a form of carbon but intense pressure in the earth has crystallised it so that it has become so hard that only a diamond can cut a diamond.

True chewing gum, which now has world-wide distribution, is made from the chicle gum of a tropical plum tree and has become an important industry to some backward countries.

Invar is a special alloy of metal which is invariable, hence its name. It does not expand or contract in the usual way and is used for the control mechanism in thermostats.

In the last war the famous Mulberry Harbour was made with concrete that floated. A special concrete was used and cast into hollow boxes.

Fibreglass, made from fine threads of molten glass, is now often used for the bodywork of cars and speedboats. It is as strong as metal and much lighter and holes can be repaired by adding fresh material.

Lignum vitae, a hard tropical wood, is so heavy that it will not float in water.

Gold is accepted throughout the world because all men value it. It is rare and beautiful and although a soft metal and easily workable, it does not tarnish or perish.

Shaving the bark of a rubber tree

man against the clock

The steam locomotive
A steam locomotive with its driving pistons and rushing wheels was one of the loveliest sights of the industrial world but now its day has gone. The locomotives were classified by a number system based on the wheels, e.g. 4-6-2. The middle figure was the number of driving wheels which were often coupled to give better grip and the others were merely idlers, supporting the machine. Stephenson's *Rocket* could do 30 m.p.h. and very soon speeds soared. In ten years 60 m.p.h. was reached and 80 m.p.h. ten years later; so rapid was development. Good track became very important to high speeds which the locomotives could easily produce. A successful world record attempt was made in eastern England in 1938 when a *Mallard* reached the speed of 126 m.p.h.

The clipper
In a last attempt to beat steam, the shipbuilders produced the clippers, their most wonderful craft. Although merchantmen, they were built like racing yachts and manned with crack crews. One of the most famous, the *Cutty Sark* has been dry-docked at Greenwich and is on permanent show. The great period was between 1840 and 1870 and the American shipyards of Baltimore and Boston were the supreme clipper builders. Soon four hundred miles were being sailed in twenty-four hours and the record from England to Australia was cut to sixty days.

Built like a racing yacht, a clipper speeding along with sails fully set

Professional cyclists in a road race

Cycling
Cycling has now become a major sport but, despite the triumphs of Reg Harris and Tommy Simpson, it is followed more successfully on the Continent. It was an Italian, Fausto Coppi who in 1942 covered 28 miles 885 yards in one hour to set the world record. The sport is split into Road Racing and Track Racing. For the latter, riders circle the track very slowly until one pulls ahead, and speeds of 40 m.p.h. are reached in the final furlong.

No doubt the greatest single attraction is the great Tour de France ridden over a distance of approximately 2,500 miles. The pace is severe, but the honour of winning the Tour de France is the supreme triumph of the professional cyclist's career.

Donald Campbell in Bluebird attempting a new water speed record on Lake Coniston

Ski-ing

The creation of the Winter Olympics for those sports which demand snow and ice and the great increase in tourists to the Winter Sports countries have made the whole world better acquainted with many exciting and spectacular sports which used to be reserved for the privileged few. The Austrians are particularly expert in the art of ski-ing and in 1956 Toni Sailer made a clean sweep, winning all four titles. The speed is terrifying. On the straight run, 100 m.p.h. has been achieved and an average of over 50 m.p.h. has been recorded over the whole of the twisting Downhill Event. The ski jump, when the competitor sails high through the air balanced like a gliding bird, is the most breathtaking sight. In 1967, Bachler of Austria made a jump of over 500 feet.

A skier competing in the Winter Olympics

The two Campbells

The world speed record attempts on water were dominated for more than a generation by the dedicated efforts of Sir Malcolm Campbell and his son Donald. Sir Malcolm began motor car racing at Brooklands in 1909 and then served as a pilot in the First World War. After the war, he made repeated attempts on the world land record with his Bluebird cars and in 1931 he recorded 245.7 m.p.h. on Daytona Beach for which he was knighted. He then set out to beat the water record, and in 1939 recorded 141.74 m.p.h. on Coniston Water. Upon his death, his son, Donald carried on. Meanwhile the Americans had raised the record for the measured mile to 282.2 m.p.h. Then, again on Coniston Water, in January 1967, Donald Campbell made a first run of 328 m.p.h. but was tragically killed on the second run, which means that the record does not stand.

Swimming

As in all other sports, records have been steadily broken by dedicated swimmers who submit themselves to long and rigorous training schedules. One amazing thing about swimming is the illusion of speed which rapid movement in water gives. Swimmers appear to be moving far faster than they actually are. Even over a fifty yard sprint, no one has yet achieved five miles an hour. Another fascinating point is that champion swimmers seem to get younger and younger. At twenty-one swimmers are old and many world records have been broken by schoolgirls in their early teens.

Britain's champion swimmer, Bobby McGregor

*Bannister finishing
the four-minute-mile*

The four-minute mile

Nothing is more remarkable in the world of speed than the way in which human athletes continue to lower all existing records by improved training methods. We have the same bodies as before the last war but a comparison of the running records shows what a difference now exists. The event which has roused most attention is the mile which stood well above four minutes before the war. Post-war athletes determined to run a mile in four minutes and the first successful breaking of this barrier took place at Oxford University where the operation was planned scientifically. Roger Bannister, a medical student now a doctor, achieved the first four-minute mile in a specially-paced attempt geared to pushing him to the limit. Wartime experience had shown that human beings fighting for survival could drive themselves through extreme exhaustion and keep going. In the past, athletes had not pushed themselves enough. The success of the attempt was no isolated freak for now more than thirty athletes have run a sub four-minute-mile and a new barrier has come into sight. The latest times are now nearer three and three quarter minutes than four minutes and the battle is on.

The stage-coach

Before the railways, those who had no private carriage were obliged to travel by stage-coach. These coaches were very slow and they trundled from inn to inn where their passengers could obtain refreshment and the horses could be changed. It was these easy stages which gave the stage-coach its name. London to York took a week at first but the new roads of the 18th century soon doubled the speed of the coaches and in 1750, the journey from London to Edinburgh was cut down to eight days. A few years later, the mail coaches with frequent fresh horses were faster still and they also carried armed guards to protect them against highwaymen. Rivalry between coachmen led to open racing on the road and soon six-in-hands were seen which took tremendous skill to handle. Wealthy young men bribed coachmen to let them drive. But the speed of the horse placed a definite limit on times and the railway easily destroyed all coaching records.

Eating

All sorts of competitions are organised against the clock, particularly in the United States. The title of the world's greatest eater goes outright to Bozo Miller, of California, who has been undefeated for nearly forty years. Miller is average height but weighs over 20 stone and is nearly five feet round the waist. He once ate twenty-seven 2-pound pullets at one sitting. In Australia a man ate 480 oysters in one hour and in England a man once ate 56 raw eggs in two minutes.

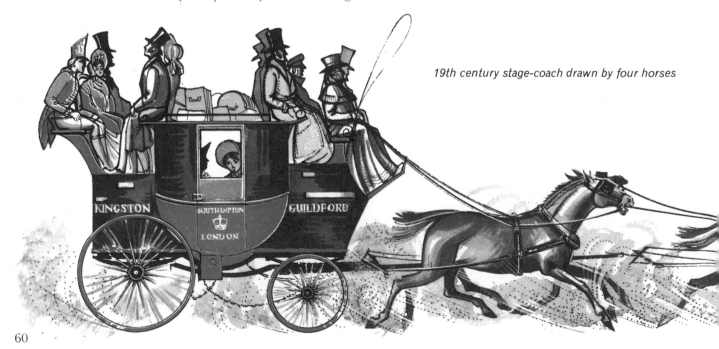

19th century stage-coach drawn by four horses

KINGSTON SOUTHAMPTON GUILDFORD LONDON

Motor car racing in the 1920s

Racing Cars

The first Benz motor car was capable of only 8-10 m.p.h. but the world record for a piston engine car is now over 400 m.p.h. and a jet-driven car, "The Spirit of America", reached over 600 m.p.h. in 1965. Apart from straight record attempts over the measured mile, motor car racing has become an international sport in all the European and American countries. The sport is divided into road racing and track racing. Road racing is not allowed in Britain but the famous Brooklands track was built in 1907. Racing cars today are remarkably similar for there is general agreement about the low-lying sleek design which is a feature of most racing cars. This type of machine is stripped of all unnecessary equipment, e.g. lights and mudguards etc., and is a single-seater. In fact, the driving seat is tailored to fit the driver. The rules covering Grand Prix racing decide the size of engine and its supercharging for a period of years. The general movement has been towards smaller cars with a higher engine performance. The modern car revs about eight times more rapidly than the old racing car.

Racing provides the motor engineer with severe test conditions for his ideas and all the tremendous improvements in family cars come from this experience. In recent years, British drivers have dominated international racing, although they have not always driven British cars.

Record-making planes

Speed in the air was high from the start, for Blériot's monoplane flew across the Channel at almost 60 m.p.h. In 1913, Jacques Schneider gave a trophy for international seaplane racing. At first, various nations won it but, with victories in 1927, 1929 and 1931, Britain won it outright using a small, stripped seaplane, the Vickers Supermarine, and in 1931, Flight-Lieutenant Stainforth flew it at 408 m.p.h. This magnificent machine became the wartime Spitfire. A little later, Whittle began work on his jet engine which was successfully flown in a Gloster plane in 1941 and the jet age had begun. High-altitude flying was introduced where the resistance and disturbance was far less and made possible by using pressurised cabins. In 1956 Peter Twiss flew a Fairy Delta at 1,132 m.p.h., the first piloted plane to reach four figures. American rocket planes, launched by a "mother" aircraft, have now doubled this speed.

The Mc-Donnell F-4B Phantom II, American high-speed, all-weather interceptor and attack fighter

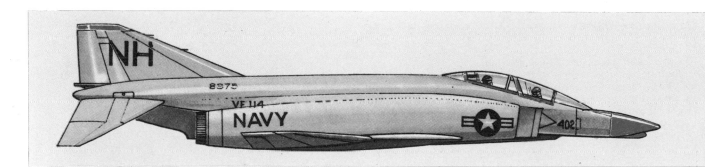

Tourist Trophy racing

The Mountain Course in the Isle of Man is the scene of the Tourist Trophy (TT) Races every June. It begins and ends at the town of Douglas and is nearly forty miles long. There are hundreds of bad corners and sharp bends and the climbs range between sea level and 1400 feet. There are races for four types of motorcycles: 500cc, 350cc, 250cc and now 125cc. Average speeds of over 100 m.p.h. are regularly achieved nowadays and the best riders are British. John Surtees, now a car driver, and Mike Hailwood have been outstanding but Italian and Japanese machines have successfully challenged British machines in recent years.

unusual plants

Orchids

Orchids are flamboyant flowers which have a vivid and startling beauty. Although about forty different types grow wild in England, the exciting ones are either grown in hothouses or found in tropical jungles. They are flowers for connoisseurs with their strange petal formations, and many expeditions have ventured deep into dangerous jungles to collect them. They grow high up in the jungle canopy in the cracks of trees where humus has collected, and some even have aerial roots to gain extra moisture. On social occasions, they are often worn with evening dress by ladies because of their extreme beauty.

This orchid is called Lady's Slipper

IT'S A FACT!

Bamboo, which grows in dense clumps and can reach a height of one hundred feet, often grows a foot in a day.

Bladderwort is an underwater plant which has a bladder with a one-way valve which acts as an insect trap which the plant gradually consumes.

Some of the drops of water seen on the surface of plant leaves in very wet conditions have not been left behind by rain but have been exuded by the plant itself to get rid of excess moisture.

Roots need air to do their work which they normally find in the spaces between the particles of soil. Consequently many plants growing in mangrove swamps have developed aerial roots to obtain their air from above.

Yeasts are cells that multiply so rapidly on sugary substances that they are seen as an active froth.

Mistletoe is a semi-parasite using the host tree, usually the apple tree, for a root and using its own leaves in the ordinary way.

The leaves of the tea plant have been used for five thousand years for brewing a drink. It is the fermentation process which makes the tea brown.

A flowering cactus

Climbing plants

All plants grow towards the sunlight so that the green chlorophyll in the leaves can do its work of building up food. Most plants have stout stems which support and arrange the leaves to the best advantage but climbing plants use other supports for this purpose. Hops grow on strings suspended from stout wires while ivy grows direct on trees, sinking roots into the tree's bark as it climbs upwards. Most of these plants produce tendrils as part of their growth which curl naturally around any available support, and many have small hooks and prickles for gaining a hold. The most amazing fact about climbing plants is that some turn one way and some the other. Most climbing plants turn anti-clockwise as they go up, but some, hops and honeysuckle are two common examples, turn clockwise. There is no simple explanation for this, the difference must lie deep in the structure of the plant.

Cacti

These desert plants are found mainly in the hotter parts of America. They have great variety of size and shape, the tallest being the Torch Thistle of Mexico which can grow to seventy feet. Almost all cacti have fierce spines or thorns and one called Prickly Pear is grown round the homes of some Mexicans as an effective fence. The purpose of the thick stems and branches is to secrete and protect water which the cacti store. The flowers are vivid and their fruits very cool and refreshing. Their flesh is also eaten as a vegetable.

Marsh Pea – a type of climbing plant

62